# Key Stage Three
# Science
# The Practice Tests

As you get towards the end of Key Stage 3, your school is likely to set you some tests to find out how you're doing in Science.

Happily, this CGP book contains three complete sets of Science practice tests so that you can go into the real thing fully prepared. We've even included detailed answers so that you can mark your own work.

## What CGP is all about

Our sole aim here at CGP is to produce the highest quality books — carefully written, immaculately presented and dangerously close to being funny.

Then we work our socks off to get them out to you — at the cheapest possible prices.

Published by CGP

Editors:
David Maliphant, Matteo Orsini Jones.

Contributors:
Paddy Gannon, Rebecca Harvey, Frederick Langridge, Jim Wilson.

With thanks to Hayley Thompson for the proofreading.
With thanks to Laura Jakubowski for the copyright research.

ISBN: 978 1 84762 254 9

Groovy website: www.cgpbooks.co.uk

Jolly bits of clipart from CorelDRAW®
Printed by Elanders Ltd, Newcastle upon Tyne

Photocopying — it's dull, it takes ages... and sometimes it's a bit naughty. Luckily, it's dead cheap,
easy and quick to order more copies of this book from CGP — just call us on 0870 750 1242. Phew!

# Contents

How to Use This Book ................................................................................................. 2

**PRACTICE PAPERS**

Paper 1A ...................................................................................................................... 4
Paper 1B ...................................................................................................................... 20

Paper 2A ...................................................................................................................... 36
Paper 2B ...................................................................................................................... 52

Paper 3A ...................................................................................................................... 68
Paper 3B ...................................................................................................................... 83

**ANSWERS**

Paper 1A ...................................................................................................................... 99
Paper 1B ...................................................................................................................... 101
Paper 2A ...................................................................................................................... 103
Paper 2B ...................................................................................................................... 105
Paper 3A ...................................................................................................................... 107
Paper 3B ...................................................................................................................... 109

# How to Use This Book

This book contains loads of practice papers for Key Stage 3 Science.
Understandably you're desperate to get started, but just hold your horses —
there are **a few things you should know** first:

## Here's What This Book Contains...

There are **three** sets of papers.
There are **answers** for all the questions and **mark schemes** at the back of the book.
Use these to mark your work **after** you've had a go at the papers.

This is what's included in **each set** of papers:

| Paper | Time Allowed | Marks Available |
|-------|--------------|-----------------|
| Paper A | 1 hour | 75 |
| Paper B | 1 hour | 75 |

## To Get the Best Marks You Need to Keep Practising

1) These practice papers won't make you better at Science, but they will show you what you **can** do, and what you **can't do**.

2) Do a test, **mark it** and look at what you got **wrong**. **That's** the stuff you need to **work on**.

3) **Go away**, **learn** those tricky bits, then **do the same test again**. If you're **still** getting questions wrong, you'll have to do even **more practice** and **test yourself again**. Keep going until you get the **best possible marks**.

4) It doesn't sound like a lot of **fun**, but it really will **help**.

## Six Top Tips for Doing Well

1) **Read everything properly**

   The most important thing is to **understand** the questions.
   Read everything **carefully** to be sure you're doing what they want.

2) **Look at the marks available**

   The **number of marks** you can get for a question gives you an idea of **how long** you should spend on that question — spend **more time** on questions worth **more marks**.

3) **Write your answers as clearly as you can**

   In a real exam, whoever's marking your paper won't be able to give you a mark if they can't read your answer — even if it's right.

4) **Check your work**

Don't throw away easy marks — even if a question looks dead simple, you have to check your answer and make sure it's sensible.

5) **Show your working**

Make sure you write down your working whenever you do a calculation. Even if you get the answer **wrong**, you could get a mark for trying to do the question in the **right way**.

6) **Use spare paper**

If you're going to do the practice papers more than once, write your answers on a separate bit of paper.

## Recording Your Progress

You can use the table below to keep a **record** of **how well you do** in each test. Don't forget to **look back** at what you got **wrong**, so you know what to **practise** for the **next test**.

## Stick Your Marks in Here:

| | | Paper A (out of 75) | Paper B (out of 75) | Total Score (out of 150) |
|---|---|---|---|---|
| Set 1 | First go | | | |
| | Second go | | | |
| | Third go | | | |
| Set 2 | First go | | | |
| | Second go | | | |
| | Third go | | | |
| Set 3 | First go | | | |
| | Second go | | | |
| | Third go | | | |

## Levels

As of **September 2014**, there are no KS3 assessment levels. But you can use the table below to see what grades you'd have been likely to get under the **old levelling system**.

You'll need to use your **total score** for a paper set.

| Mark | 150-105 | 104-73 | 72-42 | 41-36 | under 36 |
|---|---|---|---|---|---|
| Level | 7 | 6 | 5 | 4 | N |

## Key Stage 3

## Science Test

# Practice Paper 1A

Read this page, but don't open the booklet until your teacher says you can start.  Write your name and school in the spaces below.

**First Name** _____

**Last Name** _____

**School** _____

### Remember

- You have one hour to do the paper.
- Make sure you have these things with you before you start: pen, pencil, rubber, ruler, angle measurer or protractor, calculator.
- The easier questions are at the start of the paper.
- Try to answer all of the questions.
- Don't use any rough paper — write all your answers and working in this test paper.
- Check your work carefully.
- If you're not sure what to do, ask your teacher.

**1.** The diagram below shows the carbon cycle.

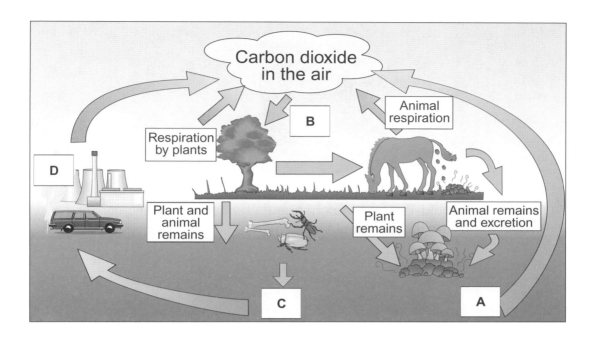

(a) Write the letters from the diagram that represent each of the following statements.

(i) Carbon compounds in fossil fuels like coal, oil and natural gas. ..........

(ii) Decomposers release carbon dioxide into the air. ..........

(iii) Photosynthesis by plants. ..........

3 marks

(b) What does letter D on the diagram represent?

........................................................................................

1 mark

Maximum 4 marks

*Science — Practice Paper 1A*

**2.**  Tim is investigating how quickly a cup of tea cools down with different amounts of tea in the cup.

(a)  What factor would Tim need to change as he carried out his investigation (the independent variable)?

..........................................................................................................

(b)  What factor would Tim need to measure as he carried out his investigation (the dependent variable)?

..........................................................................................................

(c)  Write down one factor Tim would need to keep the same to make his investigation a fair test.

..........................................................................................................

..........................................................................................................

Maximum 3 marks

**3.** The diagram shows the arrangement of particles in water as it changes state.

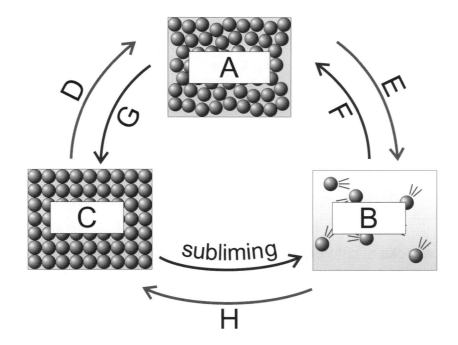

(a) Write the correct letter from the diagram next to each term below.

    (i)     Solid            ....................

    (ii)    Melting        ....................

    (iii)   Condensing    ....................

    (iv)   Liquid          ....................

    (v)    Freezing      ....................

    (vi)   Gas            ....................

    (vii)  Boiling        ....................

7 marks

(b) Give one change of state during which heat is given out.

........................................................................................................................

1 mark

Maximum 8 marks

**4.** Suzanne is looking at a cup.
Light is shining onto the cup.

(a) Describe how light from the lamp lights up the cup so Suzanne can see it.

.........................................................................................................

.........................................................................................................

.........................................................................................................

2 marks

(b) Suzanne looks at different coloured cups in different colours of light.
Fill in the empty boxes in the table to show what colour the cups appear to her.

| colour of cup | white | blue |
|---|---|---|
| colour of light | red | white |
| colour of cup to Suzanne | | |

2 marks

(c) Why does a black object look black in any light?

.........................................................................................................

1 mark

(d) In the diagram, measure the following:

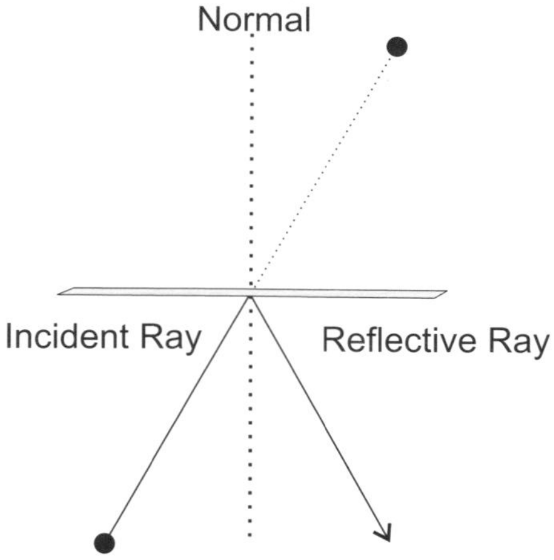

(i) The angle of incidence

.................................

(ii) The angle of reflection

.................................

(iii) The distance from the object to the mirror

.................................

(iv) The distance from the image to the mirror

.................................

4 marks

Normal

Incident Ray        Reflective Ray

Maximum 9 marks

**5.** Some metals react with acids to produce metal salts and hydrogen gas.

(a) Draw lines to join each of the metal salts below with the metal and the acid that could have reacted to produce it.

| METAL | METAL SALT | ACID | |
|-------|-----------|------|--|
| zinc | lead chloride | sulfuric acid | ☐ 1 mark |
| iron | zinc nitrate | hydrochloric acid | ☐ 1 mark |
| lead | iron sulfate | nitric acid | ☐ 1 mark |

(b) (i) What could you use to determine the pH of an acid?

...................................................................................... ☐ 1 mark

(ii) What would be observed in this pH test?

...................................................................................... ☐ 1 mark

(c) In a reaction between a metal and an acid, which reactant does the hydrogen gas that is produced come from?

...................................................................................... ☐ 1 mark

Maximum 6 marks

**6.** The diagram below shows a plant cell.

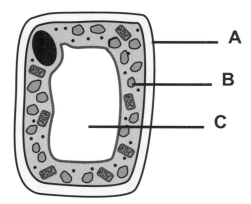

(a) Give the correct names for the structures labelled on the diagram.

A .................................................................................................................................

B .................................................................................................................................

C .................................................................................................................................

<br>

3 marks

(b) What is the function of structure A?

.................................................................................................................................

1 mark

(c) Sarah was looking at the root cells of a plant under the microscope. Why did the cells have no structures like structure B?

.................................................................................................................................

.................................................................................................................................

2 marks

Maximum 6 marks

**7.** Workers in a shoe factory use a tool to make holes in the leather.

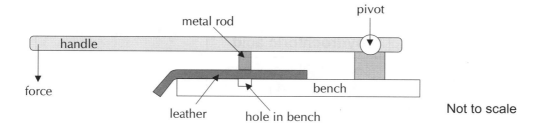

Not to scale

To punch a hole, a worker pushes the handle down.
If the force is not large enough, the tool will not punch the leather.

A worker pushes on the handle with a force of 40 N.
The following diagram shows the force on the handle.

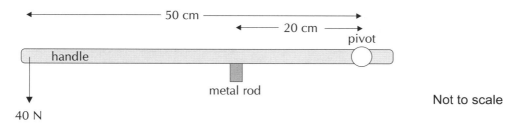

Not to scale

(a) Calculate the moment (turning effect) of the 40 N force applied to the end of the handle.  Show your working and write down the units.

..................................................................................................................

..................................................................................................................

2 marks

(b) The moment pushes the metal rod onto the leather.
What force does the rod apply to the leather?

..................................................................................................................

..................................................................................................................

1 mark

(c) A different worker uses the punch.
The metal rod pushes on the leather with a force of 80 N.

The end of the metal rod has an area of 0.5 cm$^2$.
What pressure does the rod exert on the leather?  Write down the units.

..................................................................................................................

..................................................................................................................

2 marks

Maximum 5 marks

8. Four metals were added to cold water and to dilute hydrochloric acid.
The results are shown in the table below.

| metal | with dilute hydrochloric acid | with cold water |
|---|---|---|
| nickel | some bubbles of gas form if the acid is warm | no reaction |
| potassium | (cannot be done safely) | floats, then melts, a flame appears, and sometimes there's an explosion |
| platinum | no reaction | no reaction |
| zinc | bubbles of gas form and metal dissolves slowly | no reaction |

(a)    Write the names of the **four** metals in order of reactivity.

................................. (most reactive)

.................................

.................................

............................... (least reactive)

2 marks

(b)    Name another metal, that is not in the table,
which reacts in a similar way to potassium.

......................................................................................................

1 mark

(c)    Two test tubes have been set up as shown in the diagram below.

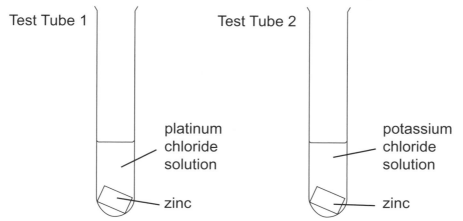

Nothing happened in Test Tube 2.
In Test Tube 1, the zinc was gradually covered with a grey deposit.

(i)    What was the grey deposit that formed in Test Tube 1?

.................................................................................................................

1 mark

(ii)   Why did no reaction take place in Test Tube 2?

.................................................................................................................

.................................................................................................................

1 mark

Maximum 5 marks

**9.**    All cigarette packets sold in Britain are now printed with a government health warning.

(a)    Tar is a chemical found in cigarette smoke.
Describe two health problems caused by tar.

1 .............................................................................................................

2 .............................................................................................................

2 marks

Continued over the page

The table below shows the percentages of low birth weight babies who had mothers who smoked during pregnancy.

| Baby's mass at birth (kg) | 2.25 or less | 2.26 – 2.70 | 2.71 – 3.15 | 3.16 – 3.60 | 3.61 – 4.05 | over 4.05 |
|---|---|---|---|---|---|---|
| % of mothers who smoked | 50 | 42 | 36 | 29 | 21 | 20 |

(b)     Plot this information as a bar chart below.

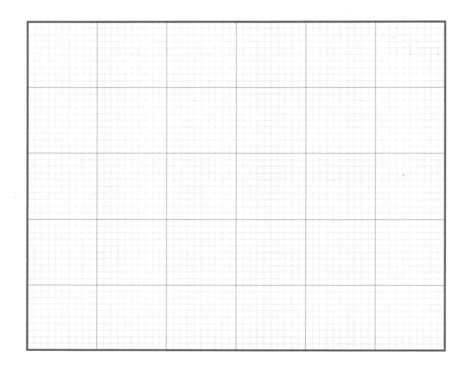

3 marks

(c)     Low birth weight has been linked with health problems in babies.
Use your bar chart to suggest why women are advised not to smoke while they are pregnant.

..................................................................................................................

..................................................................................................................

1 mark

Maximum 6 marks

**10.** John uses his empty king-size peanut butter jar to make a garden.
He keeps it in a brightly lit room with the sealed lid on.

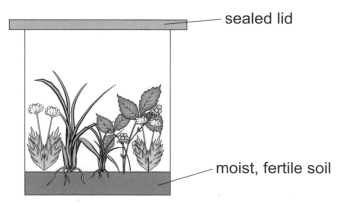

sealed lid

moist, fertile soil

Complete the following sentences to explain what happens to the carbon dioxide and oxygen levels in the jar over a week.

(a) (i) The plants use carbon dioxide in the process of:

.................................................................................................

1 mark

(ii) This process produces:

.................................................................................................

1 mark

(iii) The gas produced by the bacteria in the soil is:

.................................................................................................

1 mark

(iv) This process is called:

.................................................................................................

1 mark

Continued over the page

(b) Plants cross-pollinate by transferring pollen from one plant to another. Give two reasons why this is more likely to happen in a normal outdoor garden than in the bottled garden.

1 ................................................................................................................

...................................................................................................................

2 ................................................................................................................

...................................................................................................................

2 marks

Maximum 6 marks

11. Stefan held a piece of magnesium ribbon with tongs and placed it in a hot Bunsen flame. He saw it burn with a bright flame and produce a white ash.

(a) Write down one observation that showed that a chemical reaction had taken place.

...................................................................................................................

1 mark

(b) What is the chemical name for the white ash produced?

...................................................................................................................

1 mark

(c) Write a word equation for the chemical reaction that took place.

...................................................................................................................

1 mark

Maximum 3 marks

**12.** The diagram shows a fractional
distillation column used in a
laboratory to separate crude
oil into its different parts (called
fractions).

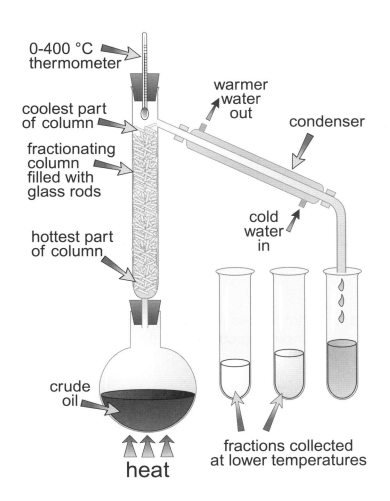

0-400 °C
thermometer

coolest part
of column

fractionating
column
filled with
glass rods

hottest part
of column

crude
oil

heat

warmer
water
out

condenser

cold
water
in

fractions collected
at lower temperatures

(a) Put a tick in the box next to the best description of crude oil below.

☐ A pure element          ☐ A pure compound

☐ A mixture of elements   ☐ A mixture of compounds

☐
1 mark

(b) The fraction being collected in the diagram is a substance called naphtha.

(i) What physical state is naphtha in while it's in the fractionating column?

..............................................................................................

☐
1 mark

(ii) Explain how the condenser works to cause the naphtha to
change state.

..............................................................................................

☐
1 mark

Maximum 3 marks

**13.** Shahana set up the following experiment to investigate the effect of light intensity on photosynthesis. Her results are shown in the table.

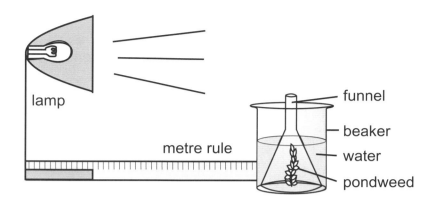

| Distance of lamp from beaker (cm) | Number of bubbles produced by pondweed in 1 minute |
|---|---|
| 100 | 2 |
| 80 | 5 |
| 60 | 9 |
| 40 | 20 |
| 20 | 39 |

(a)   Plot the results of this experiment on the axes below.
Draw a smooth curve through the points and label the axes.

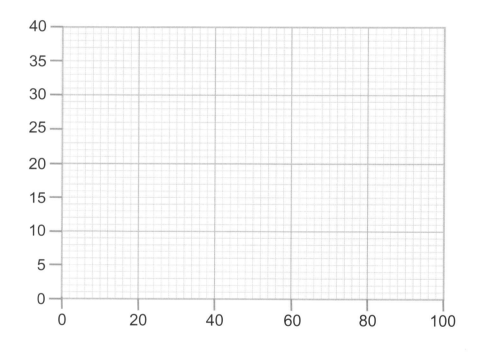

3 marks

(b)   What conclusions could Shahana draw from her results?

.........................................................................................................

.........................................................................................................

2 marks

Maximum 5 marks

**14.** Jeremy used the following circuit to investigate the resistance of different lengths of wire. For each different length of wire, he measured the voltage and the current and used these to calculate the resistance. His results are shown in the table.

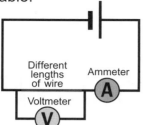

| Length of wire (cm) | Resistance (Ω) |
|---|---|
| 5 | 0.3 |
| 10 | 0.6 |
| 15 | 1.3 |
| 20 | 1.4 |
| 30 | 2.1 |
| 40 | 3.0 |

(a) (i) Plot the results on the grid below.
The first three have been done for you.

☐ 1 mark

(ii) Draw a line of best fit.

☐ 1 mark

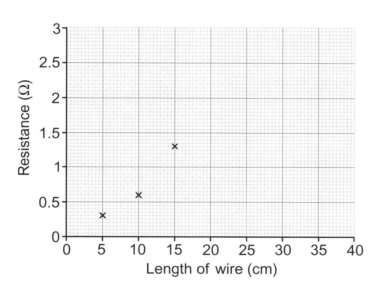

(b) One of Jeremy's results does not fit the overall pattern.
Circle this point on the graph.

☐ 1 mark

(c) Use your graph to predict:

(i) the resistance of a wire that is 25 cm long. .................. Ω

☐ 1 mark

(ii) the length of a wire with the resistance 2.5 Ω. .................. cm

☐ 1 mark

(d) Describe the relationship between resistance and wire length.

..............................................................................................................

☐ 1 mark

Maximum 6 marks

**END OF TEST**

## Key Stage 3

## Science Test

# Practice Paper 1B

Read this page, but don't open the booklet until your teacher says you can start.  Write your name and school in the spaces below.

**First Name** _____

**Last Name** _____

**School** _____

**Remember**

- You have one hour to do the paper.

- Make sure you have these things with you before you start: pen, pencil, rubber, ruler, angle measurer or protractor, calculator.

- The easier questions are at the start of the paper.

- Try to answer all of the questions.

- Don't use any rough paper — write all your answers and working in this test paper.

- Check your work carefully.

- If you're not sure what to do, ask your teacher.

**1.** Neil is making syrup by dissolving sugar in water in a beaker.

(a) Identify the solvent, solution and solute.

    (i) Solvent   ...................................................................

    (ii) Solution   ...................................................................

    (iii) Solute   ...................................................................

                                                            3 marks

(b) Suggest one thing Neil could do to the mixture
to get more sugar to dissolve.

...................................................................................................................

                                                            1 mark

                                                       Maximum 4 marks

**2.** Draw lines to match the parts of the body with the function they carry out in human digestion.

| Parts of the body | Functions |
|---|---|
| Small intestine | absorbs the water from the food waste. |
| Stomach | absorbs nutrients into the bloodstream. |
| Teeth | churns up food and mixes it with acid and enzymes. |
| Large intestine | moves food to the next part of the digestive system by peristalsis. |
| Gullet | stores waste water. |
| | grind up food and mix it with saliva. |

                                                            5 marks

                                                       Maximum 5 marks

3. The particles that make up various substances are shown below.

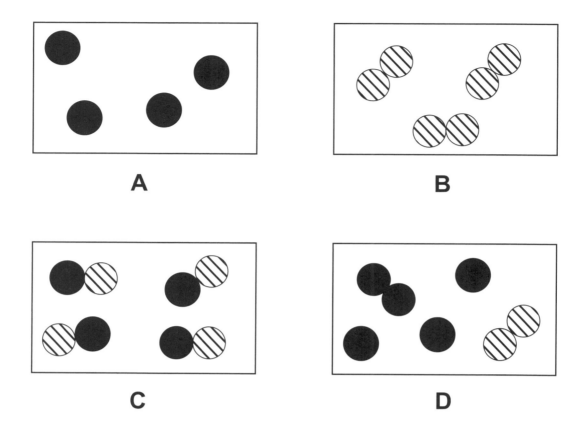

A

B

C

D

Complete the table by writing the letter of each diagram opposite its correct description.

| Description | Letter |
|---|---|
| An element made up of molecules | |
| Molecules in a compound | |
| A mixture of different elements | |
| An element made up of atoms | |

3 marks

Maximum 3 marks

**4.** James rides a motorbike to work every day. Two horizontal forces affect its motion: **forward force** and **drag**.

(a) Compare the sizes of the forward force and drag when:

(i) The bike is speeding up.

The forward force is ...................................................................

.......................................................................................................

1 mark

(ii) The bike is moving at a steady 30 miles per hour.

The forward force is ...................................................................

.......................................................................................................

1 mark

(iii) The bike is slowing down.

The forward force is ...................................................................

.......................................................................................................

1 mark

(b) The forward force occurs because the tyres are **not** able to spin on the road. What force prevents them slipping?

.......................................................................................................

1 mark

Maximum 4 marks

*Science — Practice Paper 1B*

**5.** The levels of various gases in the atmosphere vary over time, partly due to the action of green plants. During the day plants photosynthesise. Photosynthesis can be represented by the following equation:

$$\text{gas B + water} \xrightarrow[\text{CHLOROPHYLL}]{\text{LIGHT}} \text{glucose + gas A}$$

(a) Name gas A and gas B.

Gas A .................................................................................................

Gas B .................................................................................................

2 marks

At night photosynthesis stops but plants still carry out another chemical reaction which affects the levels of the two gases.

(b) What is the name of this reaction?

.................................................................................................

1 mark

(c) Write down the word equation for this reaction.

.................................................................................................

1 mark

Maximum 4 marks

**6.** Matilda is making different salts by mixing together different combinations of acids and alkalis. Name the salt produced when Matilda mixes:

(a) nitric acid and potassium hydroxide.

.................................................................................................

1 mark

(b) sulfuric acid and sodium hydroxide.

.................................................................................................

1 mark

(c) hydrochloric acid and calcium hydroxide.

.................................................................................................

1 mark

Maximum 3 marks

**7.** Keith wants to find out which snack has the highest energy content. He does an experiment to look at the amount of energy in two brands of crisps.

He burns a sample of the food to see how much this raises the temperature of the water in the test tube. This rise in temperature uses energy from the food.

(a) Suggest two things Keith should have done to make the experiment a fair test:

1. ...................................................................................................

2. ...................................................................................................

2 marks

(b) Keith should also take some precautions to increase the safety of the experiment. Give two things he could do to make the experiment safer.

1. ...................................................................................................

2. ...................................................................................................

2 marks

(c) The table shows nutritional details from the packets of the different brands.

|  | energy in kJ | protein in g | carbohydrate in g | fat in g | fibre in g |
|---|---|---|---|---|---|
| 100 g of Runners' plain crisps | 2050 | 6.2 | 56.2 | 28.7 | 4.2 |
| 100 g of Henry's Health Snack | 1300 | 9.2 | 45.1 | 10.5 | 9.1 |

Keith repeats his experiment using 10 grams of each brand.
Write down the letter of the correct statement.

A: The temperature will rise more with the Runners' Crisps.
B: The temperature change will be the same.
C: The temperature will rise more with the Henry's Health snack.

The correct statement is statement ............

1 mark

(d) Neither snack contains vitamin C. Give an example of a type of food which provides a good source of vitamin C.

...................................................................................................

1 mark

Continued over the page

(e) (i) Why is fibre an important part of a balanced diet?

.......................................................................................................

.......................................................................................................

1 mark

(ii) Using the table, give **two** reasons why Henry's Health Snacks are healthier than Runners' plain crisps.

.......................................................................................................

.......................................................................................................

2 marks

Maximum 9 marks

8. The diagram shows the rock cycle. Write the correct letter from the diagram next to each of the labels given below.

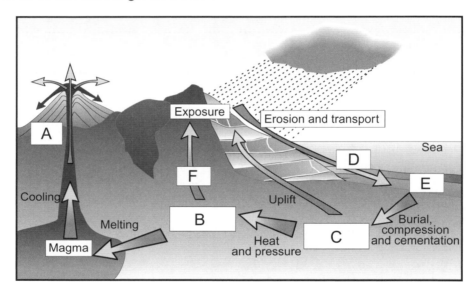

| Label | Letter |
| --- | --- |
| (a) Metamorphic rocks | ............................ |
| (b) Igneous rocks | ............................ |
| (c) Deposition | ............................ |
| (d) Sediments | ............................ |
| (e) Sedimentary rocks | ............................ |

5 marks

Maximum 5 marks

**9.** Ruby is investigating displacement reactions.
The diagram shows her experiment and its results.

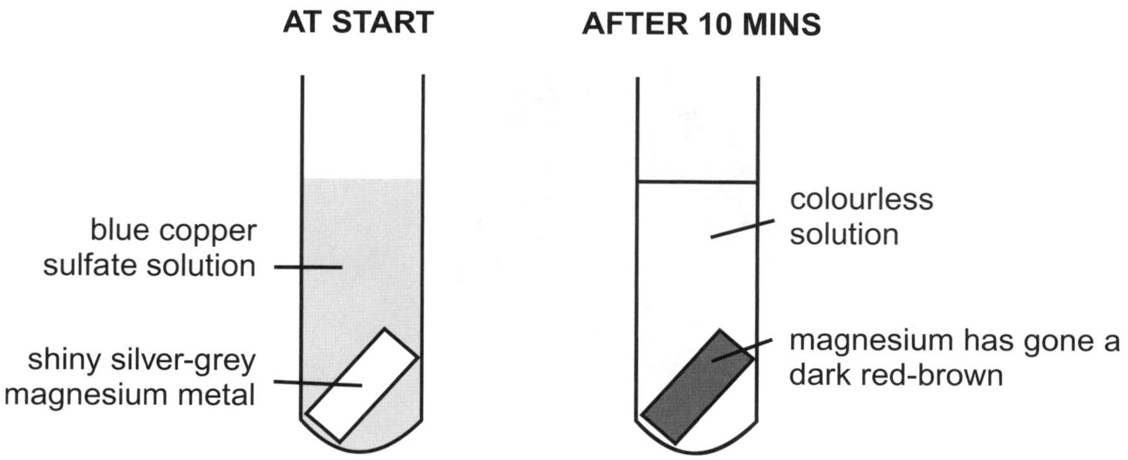

AT START      AFTER 10 MINS

blue copper sulfate solution

shiny silver-grey magnesium metal

colourless solution

magnesium has gone a dark red-brown

(a) Write a word equation for the displacement reaction in Ruby's investigation.

.......................................................................................................

.......................................................................................................

2 marks

(b) Explain why this type of reaction is called a displacement reaction.

.......................................................................................................

.......................................................................................................

1 mark

(c) Which of the two metals involved in the reaction was the more reactive?

.......................................................................................................

1 mark

Maximum 4 marks

**10.** Peter lives in England.  He is talking on the telephone to his friend Manuel, who lives in Ecuador.  Ecuador is a country which lies on the Earth's equator.

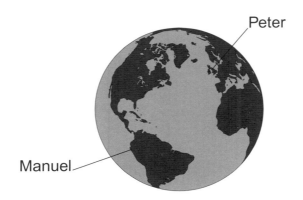

**Peter** says, "It's summer here.  The days are eighteen hours long and it gets really hot — 25 °C sometimes."

**Manuel** says, "The days are always about twelve hours long here and the temperature often reaches 35 °C."

(a)  When it's summer in England, why does England have longer days than Ecuador?

.........................................................................................................

.........................................................................................................

2 marks

(b)  Having longer days is one reason why it gets hot in summer in England. Explain another reason why it gets hot in summer in England.

.........................................................................................................

.........................................................................................................

2 marks

Maximum 4 marks

**11.** Jill did an experiment to investigate how quickly marble chips dissolve in different concentrations of hydrochloric acid. As the reaction proceeded she recorded the mass of the beaker containing the reaction mixture at five minute intervals. The apparatus she used is shown below.

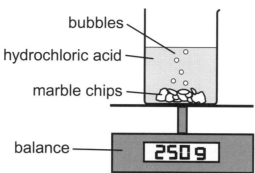

(a) What factor did Jill change as she carried out her investigation (the independent variable)?

.....................................................................................................

1 mark

(b) Give two factors she should have kept the same to make it a fair test.

1. ..............................................................................................

2. ..............................................................................................

2 marks

(c) What could Jill do to make her results more reliable?

.....................................................................................................

.....................................................................................................

1 mark

(d) The table shows the results obtained from Jill's first experiment. She used 220 g of marble chips.

| Time (mins) | Mass of beaker and contents (g) |
|---|---|
| 0 | 250.0 |
| 5 | 245.0 |
| 10 | 242.0 |
| 15 | 240.5 |
| 20 | 239.5 |
| 25 | 239.5 |

Continued over the page

(i)   Draw a fully labelled graph to show these results on the grid below, joining the points with a smooth curve.

3 marks

(ii)  Describe the trend shown by the results.

..............................................................................................................

1 mark

(iii) The reaction stopped at one of the times listed below.
Tick the correct box.

☐ 14 minutes          ☐ 18½ minutes

☐ 22½ minutes         ☐ 25 minutes

1 mark

(iv)  By how much did the mass of the beaker and its contents decrease in 25 minutes?

..............................................................................................................

2 marks

Maximum 11 marks

**12.** At a theatre red, green and blue spotlights are used.

An actress is wearing a yellow dress. However, when the red and blue spotlights shine on her, the dress appears red.

(a) Explain why the dress appears red when only the red and blue spotlights are shining on it.

.................................................................................................

.................................................................................................

☐

2 marks

(b) When only a red and a green spotlight are shining on it, the dress appears yellow. Explain why.

.................................................................................................

.................................................................................................

☐

2 marks

(c) Predict what colour the dress would look when all three lights are used.

.................................................................................................

☐

1 mark

Maximum 5 marks

**13.** When Liam fell off his bike, he dislocated his shoulder. A doctor examined Liam's shoulder joint and the muscle surrounding it.

(a) Muscles work in antagonistic pairs. What does this mean?

..............................................................................................................

..............................................................................................................

2 marks

The diagram shows the bones and muscles in the arm.

(b) Which of the muscles in the diagram, **A**, **B**, **C** or **D**, contracts to bend the arm at the elbow?

..............................................................................................................

1 mark

Maximum 3 marks

**14.** The diagram shows an electromagnet used to control a device for locking a door.

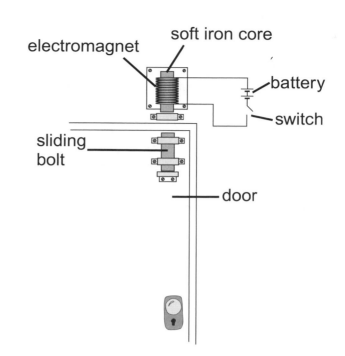

electromagnet   soft iron core

battery

switch

sliding bolt

door

When the electromagnet is switched on, the door is locked.

When the electromagnet is switched off, the door is unlocked.

(a)     The sliding bolt is made from a magnetic material.
Draw an arrow on the diagram to show which way the sliding bolt moves when the electromagnet is switched on.

1 mark

(b)     What is the name of the force that moves the bolt when the electromagnet is switched **off**?

..................................................................................................................

1 mark

(c)     Suggest a material the bolt could be made from.

..................................................................................................................

1 mark

(d)     Write down one way of making the electromagnet stronger.

..................................................................................................................

1 mark

Maximum 4 marks

**15.** Read the following description of a garden ecosystem
and answer the questions that follow.

> The 'cabbage white' butterfly feeds on brassica plants. It shares this food
> source with slugs and snails, but the slugs and snails will also
> eat lettuce. Small birds like blue tits and thrushes eat the butterflies, slugs
> and snails. Cats eat the blue tits and the thrushes.

(a)     Draw out the food web in the space provided.

3 marks

(b)     Why is it harder to collect reliable data when working in the field than when
working in the laboratory?  Tick the correct box.

☐     It's hard to get a large enough sample.

☐     There are many variables that cannot be controlled when working in the field.

☐     Scientists cannot record their data properly when they work outdoors.

1 mark

(c)     Suggest a way that slugs and snails could be counted in a garden.

..............................................................................................................

(d)     A gardener uses slug pellets to kill slugs and snails, to stop them
        eating his plants.
        Describe and explain the effect you would expect this to have on the
        number of blue tits in the garden.

..............................................................................................................

..............................................................................................................

..............................................................................................................

Maximum 7 marks

**END OF TEST**

# Science
## KEY STAGE 3
### PRACTICE PAPER 2A

# Key Stage 3

# Science Test

# Practice Paper 2A

Read this page, but don't open the booklet until your teacher says you can start. Write your name and school in the spaces below.

**First Name** _____

**Last Name** _____

**School** _____

**Remember**

- You have one hour to do the paper.
- Make sure you have these things with you before you start: pen, pencil, rubber, ruler, angle measurer or protractor, calculator.
- The easier questions are at the start of the paper.
- Try to answer all of the questions.
- Don't use any rough paper — write all your answers and working in this test paper.
- Check your work carefully.
- If you're not sure what to do, ask your teacher.

**1.** Tick the boxes to show whether each part of the body listed below is a cell, a tissue or an organ.  The first one has been done for you.

|  | cell | tissue | organ |
|---|---|---|---|
| Stomach | ☐ | ☐ | ✓ |
| Muscle | ☐ | ☐ | ☐ |
| Heart | ☐ | ☐ | ☐ |
| Sperm | ☐ | ☐ | ☐ |
| Brain | ☐ | ☐ | ☐ |
| Neurone | ☐ | ☐ | ☐ |

3 marks

Maximum 3 marks

**2.** Digestion is the process by which food is broken down and absorbed into the bloodstream.  The diagram below shows part of the digestive system.

(a) Give the name of each part labelled A to D.

A is the ...................................................................................

B is the ...................................................................................

C is the ...................................................................................

D is the ...................................................................................

4 marks

(b) Why does food need to be broken down before it is absorbed into the bloodstream?

...................................................................................

1 mark

Maximum 5 marks

3. Sally has three rocks. She wants to find out what type of rock each one is.
The three types of rock are igneous, sedimentary and metamorphic.
Use the clues below to help Sally identify her rocks.

(a) Rock 1 is made of distinct layers. There is a fossil in it.

This rock is ..................................... rock.

1 mark

(b) Rock 2 also has layers, but they are 'wavy'.
There are some small crystals visible.

This rock is ..................................... rock.

1 mark

(c) Rock 3 has no layers and is made of lots of crystals.

This rock is ..................................... rock.

1 mark

Maximum 3 marks

4. Animals get characteristics from their parents.

Complete the following sentences:

(a) Information about an animal's characteristics is passed on in a

molecule called ...........................

1 mark

(b) The female's genes are passed on in the egg.

The male's genes are passed on in the ...........................

1 mark

(c) The genes are held in the ........................... of the cells.

1 mark

(d) The process of passing characteristics by genes has a special name.

We say the children ........................... characteristics

from their parents.

1 mark

Maximum 4 marks

**5.** The diagram below shows the apparatus used to obtain pure water from impure water.

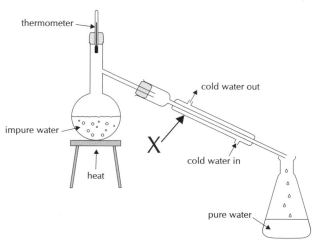

thermometer

cold water out

impure water

X

cold water in

heat

pure water

(a) What is the name of this
process of purifying water? ..................................................

☐ 1 mark

(b) If you were to carry out this process, what
temperature would the thermometer show? ............. °C

☐ 1 mark

(c) The diagram shows a piece of apparatus labelled **X**. What is its function?

.........................................................................................................................

.........................................................................................................................

☐ 1 mark

The following diagram shows
particles in three states: solid, liquid
and gas. The arrows (1, 2, 3 and 4)
represent changes of state.

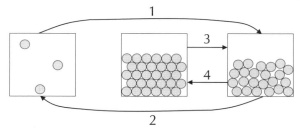

1

3

4

2

(d) Write down the names of the four changes of
state. Choose from the words in the box.

1 ...................................

2 ...................................

3 ...................................

4 ...................................

condensing    melting

bubbling      boiling

filtering

freezing

evaporating

☐ 4 marks

(e) Give the number (1, 2, 3 or 4) for the change of state which occurs in
the following places in the apparatus from parts (a), (b) and (c).

in piece of apparatus labelled X ..........

in the flask containing impure water ..........

☐ 1 mark

Maximum 8 marks

*Science — Practice Paper 2A*

**6.** Tina used the apparatus shown below to investigate how an electric heater heats up an aluminium block.

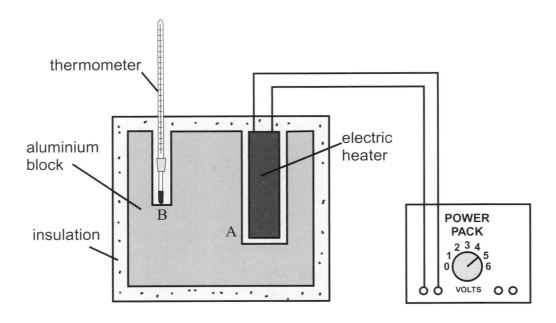

Here are her results:

| Time (min) | Temperature (°C) |
|:---:|:---:|
| 0 | 20 |
| 5 | 28 |
| 10 | 35 |
| 15 | 45 |
| 20 | 52 |
| 25 | 61 |
| 30 | 68 |

(a)  What process causes heat from point A to reach point B?

..............................................................................................................................

1 mark

(b)  Use these results to draw a graph on the grid on the next page.

Decide the scale for each axis and label them clearly.
Plot the points.
Draw a line of best fit.

41

3 marks

(c) Tina predicts that all metals will heat up at the same rate.
Describe how she could test this prediction using the apparatus.

.......................................................................................................................

.......................................................................................................................

2 marks

(d) What was the temperature of the aluminium block at 22 minutes?

.......................................................................................................................

1 mark

(e) Give **one** reason why it is more useful to present the results as a
line graph rather than a table?

.......................................................................................................................

1 mark

Maximum 8 marks

7.    An ice cube was placed in a beaker of water and the temperature of the water was measured every minute for 30 minutes.  The water was originally at room temperature.

The results are shown on the graph below.

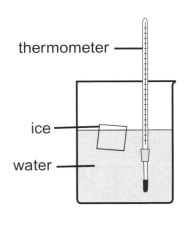
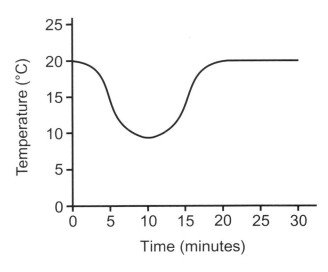

(a)    What physical change do you think happened to the ice between 0 and 10 minutes?

........................................................................................................

1 mark

(b)    How did the kinetic energy of the ice particles change during this time?

........................................................................................................

1 mark

(c)    How did the kinetic energy of the water particles change during this time?

........................................................................................................

1 mark

(d)    What was the minimum temperature reached by the water?

........................................................................................................

1 mark

(e)    What was the room temperature during this experiment?

........................................................................................................

1 mark

Maximum 5 marks

**8.** Newlands School has a wind turbine for generating electricity.

(a) Complete the sentence below to describe the useful energy change that happens when the wind turbine is generating electricity.

The wind turbine changes ...................................................... energy

into electrical energy for the school.

1 mark

(b) Write down one advantage of using a wind turbine to make electricity instead of using mains electricity.

......................................................................................................

1 mark

(c) Write down one disadvantage of using a wind turbine to make electricity instead of using mains electricity.

......................................................................................................

1 mark

(d) Electricity can also be created using coal, oil and gas.
What is the ultimate source of the energy that these resources contain?

......................................................................................................

1 mark

Maximum 4 marks

**9.** Jill carried out chromatography on samples of three known substances, A, B and C, and two unknown substances, X and Y.

Her results are shown in the diagram.

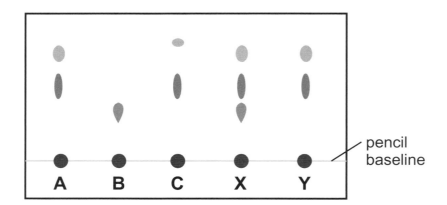

(a)   Which two substances are the same?

..............................................................................................................................

1 mark

(b)   Which two known substances make up substance X?

..............................................................................................................................

1 mark

(c)   Explain why the baseline is drawn in pencil and not in ink.

..............................................................................................................................

..............................................................................................................................

1 mark

(d)   Jill put the baseline above the solvent surface, not below it.
Explain why.

..............................................................................................................................

..............................................................................................................................

1 mark

Maximum 4 marks

10. Electricity meters measure the amount of electrical energy used, in units of kilowatt-hours (kWh). The diagram below shows how the meter reading in Joe's house changed over 24 hours.

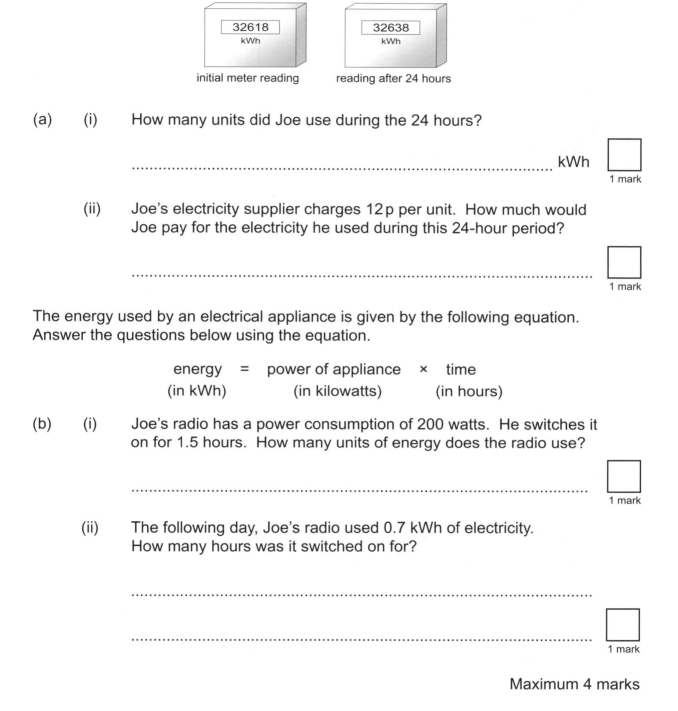

| 32618 | 32638 |
| --- | --- |
| kWh | kWh |
| initial meter reading | reading after 24 hours |

(a) (i) How many units did Joe use during the 24 hours?

...................................................................................... kWh

1 mark

(ii) Joe's electricity supplier charges 12p per unit. How much would Joe pay for the electricity he used during this 24-hour period?

......................................................................................

1 mark

The energy used by an electrical appliance is given by the following equation. Answer the questions below using the equation.

$$\text{energy} = \text{power of appliance} \times \text{time}$$
(in kWh)        (in kilowatts)        (in hours)

(b) (i) Joe's radio has a power consumption of 200 watts. He switches it on for 1.5 hours. How many units of energy does the radio use?

......................................................................................

1 mark

(ii) The following day, Joe's radio used 0.7 kWh of electricity. How many hours was it switched on for?

......................................................................................

......................................................................................

1 mark

Maximum 4 marks

Mr Jones has a light inside his caravan. It uses a battery.

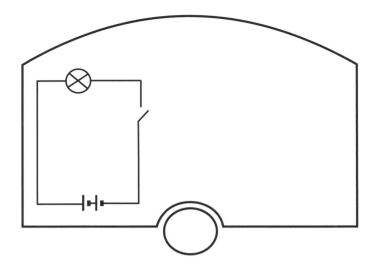

Mr Jones decides he wants another light that he can switch on when he needs it.

(a) Complete the diagram below to show how he should connect up the lights in his caravan. Include the light switches.

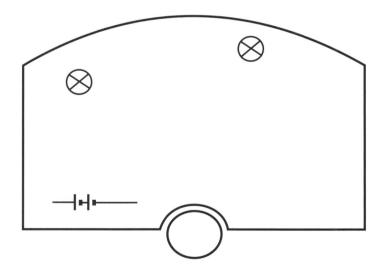

3 marks

(b) What problem might Mr Jones expect if he uses both lights in his caravan? Give a reason.

....................................................................................................................

....................................................................................................................

2 marks

Maximum 5 marks

**12.** Hot magnesium ribbon reacts with steam to produce magnesium oxide and hydrogen.

(a) Write a word equation for the reaction described above.

...................................................................................................... ☐
1 mark

(b) Potassium reacts with cold water to produce a gas and a solution that turns universal indicator solution dark blue.

(i) Write a word equation for this chemical reaction.

...................................................................................................... 

...................................................................................................... ☐
2 marks

(ii) Is the resulting solution an acid, an alkali or neutral?

...................................................................................................... ☐
1 mark

(iii) Tick the pH value you would expect for the dark blue solution.

☐ 0    ☐ 1    ☐ 4    ☐ 7    ☐ 12    ☐
1 mark

Maximum 5 marks

**13.** Plants need to take in water from the soil.
Dr Gabion decided to do an experiment to find out if there
is anything else in the soil which plants use for growth.

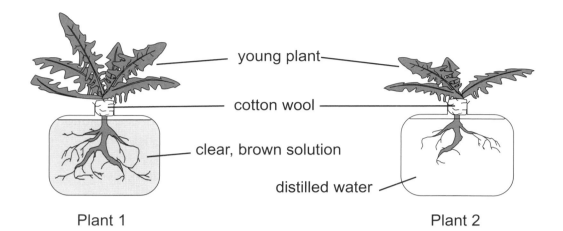

young plant

cotton wool

clear, brown solution

distilled water

Plant 1                                Plant 2

Dr Gabion made the clear, brown solution for Plant 1
by mixing up soil and water, and then separating the
soil particles out to leave the clear, brown solution.

(a)    What method could Dr Gabion use to separate the soil particles from
the brown solution?

..................................................................................................................

..................................................................................................................

1 mark

(b)    Why did Dr Gabion grow one plant in distilled water?

..................................................................................................................

..................................................................................................................

1 mark

(c)  (i)  What type of substances are in the clear, brown solution that the plant uses for growth?

.......................................................................................................

1 mark

(ii)  Explain how roots are adapted to take in water.

.......................................................................................................

.......................................................................................................

1 mark

(d)  Dr Gabion carried out another experiment with three similar plants. The solutions in each container were the same.  He put all the plants in a sunny place.  The pictures below show the result of the experiment.

| Plant 3 | Plant 4 | Plant 5 |
|---|---|---|
| The container holds the clear, brown solution. The container and leaves are wrapped in black plastic. | The container holds the clear, brown solution. The leaves are wrapped in black plastic. | The container holds the clear, brown solution. The container is wrapped in black plastic. |

Of the three plants, Plant 5 was the only one which grew well. Explain why.

.......................................................................................................

.......................................................................................................

1 mark

Maximum 5 marks

**14.** Julie is a skydiver. As she falls to Earth the forces on her change and affect her speed. Here are some possible reasons for her different speeds.

**A**     Her weight is greater than the air resistance.

**B**     Her weight is less than the air resistance.

**C**     Her weight is equal to the air resistance.

**D**     She has no weight.

**E**     There is no air resistance.

Choose from these reasons to explain each of the following things that happen to Julie. Write the correct letter next to each description.

| What happens to Julie | Reason | |
|---|---|---|
| (a)  When she first jumps out of the aeroplane she falls faster and faster. | ...................... | ☐ 1 mark |
| (b)  Eventually she reaches a steady speed, moving very fast. | ...................... | ☐ 1 mark |
| (c)  She slows down suddenly when her parachute opens. | ...................... | ☐ 1 mark |
| (d)  She falls at a steady speed, more slowly than before. | ...................... | ☐ 1 mark |

(e)     Julie falls 100 metres in 15 seconds. Calculate her speed.

........................................................................................................

........................................................................................................     ☐ 2 marks

Maximum 6 marks

**15.** Dylan compared two indigestion tablets, A and B, to see which was better at neutralising stomach acid (hydrochloric acid). The active ingredient in both tablets was calcium carbonate.

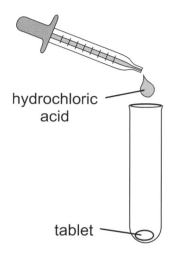

hydrochloric acid

tablet

He put each tablet in a separate test tube and added hydrochloric acid, one drop at a time, until no further reaction occurred. He recorded the number of drops needed to neutralise each tablet.
His results are shown below.

| Tablet | No. of drops needed |
|--------|---------------------|
| A | 22 |
| B | 30 |

(a) Which tablet was better at neutralising stomach acid? Explain your answer.

........................................................................................................

2 marks

(b) Give two factors that Dylan should have kept the same to make the comparison a fair test.

1. ....................................................................................................

2. ....................................................................................................

2 marks

(c) What factor did Dylan change as he carried out his investigation (the independent variable)?

........................................................................................................

1 marks

(d) Give one way in which Dylan could improve the experiment to make the results more reliable.

........................................................................................................

........................................................................................................

1 mark

Maximum 6 marks

**END OF TEST**

# Key Stage 3

# Science Test

# Practice Paper 2B

**Remember**

- You have one hour to do the paper.

- Make sure you have these things with you before you start: pen, pencil, rubber, ruler, angle measurer or protractor, calculator.

- The easier questions are at the start of the paper.

- Try to answer all of the questions.

- Don't use any rough paper — write all your answers and working in this test paper.

- Check your work carefully.

- If you're not sure what to do, ask your teacher.

**1.** The chemical formula for a common salt is: **CuSO$_4$**

(a) Write down the names of all the elements in this compound and state how many atoms of each are present.

.......................................................................................................

.......................................................................................................

.......................................................................................................

3 marks

(b) Name the salt.

.......................................................................................................

1 mark

Maximum 4 marks

ecker bus has some mirrors to let the driver see the passengers up deck.

(a)   On the diagram, draw the path of a ray of light to show how the driver sees the naughty child upstairs.  Use a ruler.

2 marks

(b)   Cyclists often use special reflectors that shine in the dark so that drivers behind them can see them.  The reflector always sends light back to where it came from.

Complete the diagram to show how the reflector sends light back to where it came from.

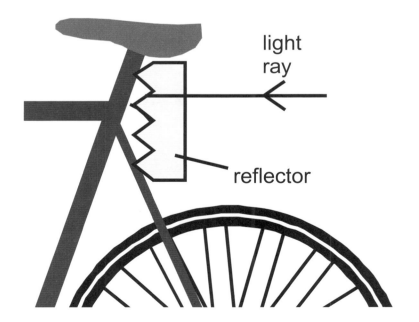

light ray

reflector

2 marks

Maximum 4 marks

**3.** The diagram shows a generalised human body cell.

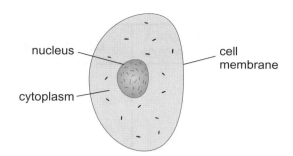

(a) Draw lines to match up the parts of the cell with their function.

| Nucleus | | controls what passes into and out of the cell. |
|---|---|---|
| Cytoplasm | | controls the cell. |
| Cell membrane | | where all the chemical reactions take place. |

2 marks

(b) (i) Name the chemical process that happens in all body cells to release energy.

.......................................................................................................

1 mark

(ii) For each of these substances, tick the correct box to show whether it is used or made during this process.

|  | **Used** | **Made** |
|---|---|---|
| Oxygen | ☐ | ☐ |
| Glucose | ☐ | ☐ |
| Carbon dioxide | ☐ | ☐ |

3 marks

(iii) Name the process by which oxygen enters cells.

.......................................................................................................

1 mark

Maximum 7 marks

*Science — Practice Paper 2B*

**4.** The following table contains some data about different species of bird within a community.

| Species of bird | Average no. of eggs laid per year by a female bird | % death rate per year |
|---|---|---|
| A | 8 | 35 |
| B | 1 | 10 |
| C | 3 | 8 |
| D | 5 | 40 |
| E | 11 | 48 |
| F | 6 | 18 |

(a)     Plot this information as a scatter graph on the axes below.  Draw a line of best fit.

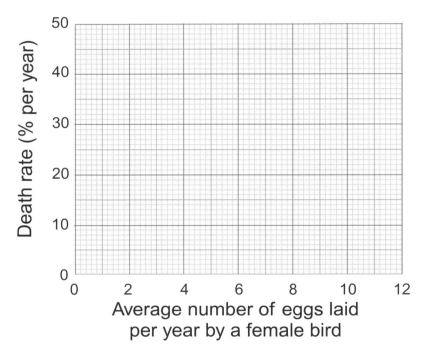

3 marks

(b)     Look at the graph you have plotted.  Which species do you think has an unusually high death rate considering its annual egg production?

.................................................................................................................

1 mark

(c)     If 30% of bluetits die each year, use your graph to estimate the number of eggs laid per year by the average female bluetit.

.................................................................................................................

1 mark

Maximum 5 marks

**5.** A pupil is using the apparatus shown below to investigate how strong different magnets are.

He tests two magnets, A and B.

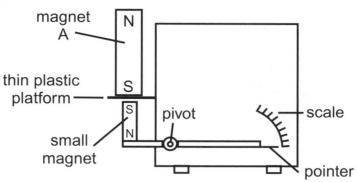

(a) Explain what happens to the small magnet when magnet A is placed on the platform as shown.

...................................................................................................................

...................................................................................................................

2 marks

(b) Why is it important to put the two south poles next to each other?

...................................................................................................................

...................................................................................................................

2 marks

(c) Suggest a reason why the pivot has been placed nearer to the small magnet than to the pointer.

...................................................................................................................

...................................................................................................................

1 mark

(d) How can the pupil tell which is the stronger magnet, A or B?

...................................................................................................................

...................................................................................................................

1 mark

Maximum 6 marks

6.  Becky says that if she blows through a straw into water, the carbon dioxide in her breath will turn the water acidic.  She does an experiment to test this. Her apparatus and results are shown below.

20 cm³ water with universal indicator — green colour

orange colour

**START**  **AFTER 2 MINUTES**

(a) What conclusion can you draw from Becky's results?

......................................................................................................

......................................................................................................

2 marks

(b) Huang says that Becky should have repeated the experiment using ordinary air as a control.  He does this, using an air pump instead of blowing out, and finds that after two minutes the solution is still green. What conclusion can you draw from Huang's results?

......................................................................................................

......................................................................................................

2 marks

(c) How do the two experiments support Becky's statement?

......................................................................................................

......................................................................................................

......................................................................................................

2 marks

Maximum 6 marks

**7.** A bell jar can be used to demonstrate the mechanism of breathing.

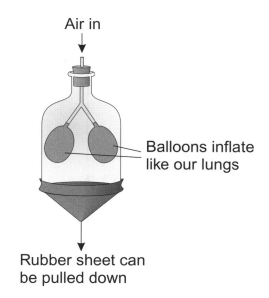

Air in

Balloons inflate like our lungs

Rubber sheet can be pulled down

As the rubber sheet is pulled down, air rushes in to fill the balloons. The balloons represent our lungs.

(a) Which part of our respiratory system does the rubber sheet represent?

.................................................................................................

1 mark

(b) Why does air rush in when the rubber sheet is pulled down?

.................................................................................................

1 mark

(c) What would happen to the balloons if the rubber sheet was then let go? Explain your answer.

.................................................................................................

.................................................................................................

2 marks

(d) Smoking can cause damage to the lungs, leading to difficulty in breathing. Name one chemical contained in cigarette smoke that can harm the lungs.

.................................................................................................

1 mark

Maximum 5 marks

**8.** The diagram shows how extrusive and intrusive igneous rocks are formed.

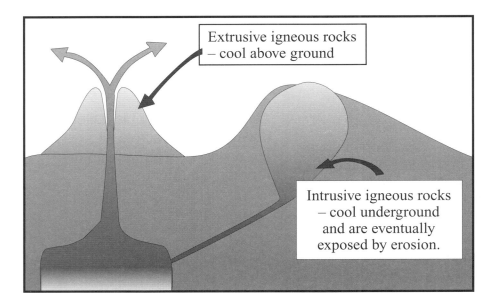

Extrusive igneous rocks – cool above ground

Intrusive igneous rocks – cool underground and are eventually exposed by erosion.

Below are diagrams showing the crystals in two igneous rock samples, A and B.

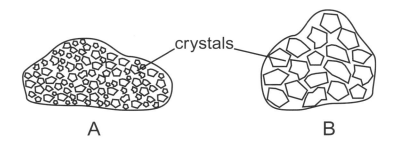

crystals

A                    B

(a) Which rock sample is an intrusive igneous rock?  Explain your answer.

......................................................................................................................

......................................................................................................................

2 marks

(b) Draw lines to connect each of the rocks below to the correct rock type.

| Marble | | Sedimentary |
| Limestone | | Igneous |
| Granite | | Metamorphic |

2 marks

Maximum 4 marks

**9.** Mark and Bill were letting toy cars roll down a ramp onto a wooden floor to see how far they went.

The cars all stopped at different points after travelling across the floor.

(a) Name a force that acts to slow down and stop the cars.

..............................................................................................................

1 mark

(b) They measured the distances travelled by four cars.
Their results are shown in the table.

| CAR | DISTANCE TRAVELLED (cm) |
|-----|-------------------------|
| 1 | 50 |
| 2 | 22 |
| 3 | 30 |
| 4 | 37 |

Complete the following bar chart showing the distance travelled by each car.

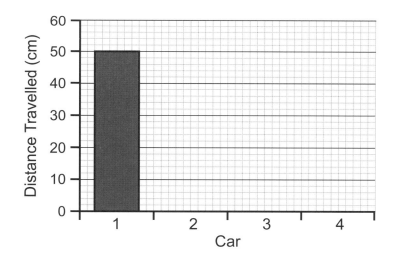

2 marks

(c) Suggest three reasons why the cars travelled different distances.

..............................................................................................................

..............................................................................................................

3 marks

Maximum 6 marks

needs to buy a light bulb. She has to choose between an ordinary ...ment bulb and a 20 watt low-energy bulb. Both bulbs give out the ...ount of light energy, but the low-energy bulb uses less electrical energy.

...dvertising panel beside the low energy bulbs says:

> A low energy bulb only uses 20% of the energy used by an equivalent filament bulb. A low energy bulb lasts eight times as long as a filament bulb. A low energy bulb saves you money in the long term.

(a)   What happens to the energy that is not converted to light in the filament bulb?

......................................................................................................... ☐

1 mark

(b)   Write down one other piece of information Mrs Goldsmith needs before she can decide whether the low-energy bulb really is cheaper in the long term.

.........................................................................................................

......................................................................................................... ☐

1 mark

(c)   Write down two reasons why Mrs Goldsmith might decide to buy the low-energy bulb even if it works out to be more expensive in the long run.

1. ....................................................................................................

2. .................................................................................................... ☐

2 marks

(d)   Mrs Goldsmith also needs to replace an ordinary 60 watt filament bulb. Which low energy bulb should she choose? Tick the correct box.

☐ 20 watt      ☐ 16 watt      ☐ 12 watt      ☐ 8 watt      ☐

1 mark

Maximum 5 marks

**11.** This picture shows an archer.
He holds the arrow and pulls it back to fire it.

string   bow   arrow

(a)   At the moment shown in the picture, two **horizontal** forces act on the arrow: the force exerted by the string and the force exerted by the archer's fingers. The arrow **isn't** moving.

The archer pulls the arrow back and holds it with a force of 120 N.
Predict the force exerted by the string on the arrow.

.........................N

☐ 1 mark

(b)   The archer releases the arrow and it moves forward.  Explain why this happens.

...................................................................................................................

...................................................................................................................

☐ 1 mark

(c)   While the arrow is flying across the field, **two** forces act on it.  Gravity acts downwards and air resistance acts in the opposite direction to the movement. Explain why these forces **can't** balance each other, even if they are equal.

...................................................................................................................

...................................................................................................................

☐ 1 mark

(d)   The arrow hits a target.  The end of the arrow is pointed and sharp so that it exerts a large pressure on the target.
Explain why a blunt end would exert a lower pressure on the target.

...................................................................................................................

...................................................................................................................

☐ 1 mark

Maximum 4 marks

**12.** Rahel heated 28.5 g of zinc powder in air. The mass of the white powder left behind after heating was 30.5 g.

(a) Explain why the mass of the products is never less than the mass of the reactants.

..................................................................................................................

1 mark

(b) (i) What substance reacted with the zinc metal?

..................................................................................................................

1 mark

(ii) Calculate the mass of this substance that reacted.

..................................................................................................................

1 mark

(c) Write down the chemical name of the powder formed after burning.

..................................................................................................................

1 mark

Maximum 4 marks

**13.** The diagram below shows "Hero's Engine". This was the first machine to demonstrate steam power. Water is boiled in the large bowl. Steam travels through the tubes supporting the revolving ball and is ejected through the two 'jets' attached to the sphere, causing it to spin.

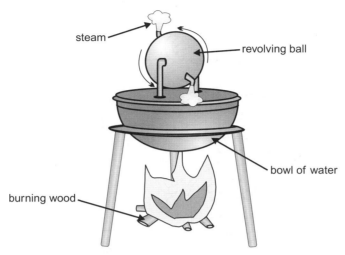

(a) What 'change of state' happens to water when it boils?

..................................................................................................................................

1 mark

(b) Starting with the energy in the wood, describe the energy transformations that occur in Hero's Engine.

..................................................................................................................................

..................................................................................................................................

..................................................................................................................................

3 marks

(c) Wood is a renewable energy source.
Name two non-renewable energy sources.

1. .........................................................................................................................

2. .........................................................................................................................

2 marks

Maximum 6 marks

**14.** Look at the diagram below showing part of the human skeleton.

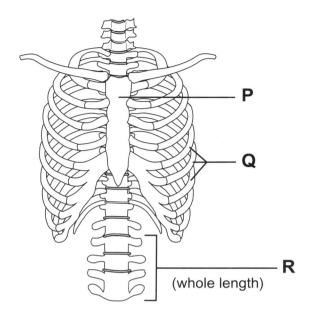

(a)    Write down the names of the structures P, Q and R in the spaces below.

P        ..............................................................................

Q        ..............................................................................

R        ..............................................................................

3 marks

(b)    The skeleton is designed for movement, support and protection.
        Which of these is the primary function of:

(i)     Structure Q? ...................................................................

1 mark

(ii)    Structure R? ....................................................................

1 mark

Maximum 5 marks

**15.** Part of the reactivity series of elements is shown on the right.

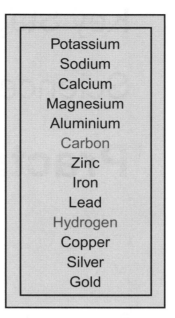

Potassium
Sodium
Calcium
Magnesium
Aluminium
Carbon
Zinc
Iron
Lead
Hydrogen
Copper
Silver
Gold

Use this information to complete the table below, which shows what happened when samples of different metals were added to solutions of various metal salts.

Use a tick (✓) to show a reaction, and a cross (✗) to show no reaction.

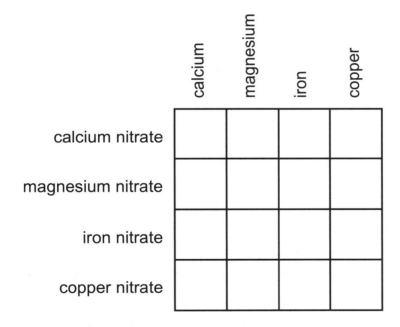

|  | calcium | magnesium | iron | copper |
|---|---|---|---|---|
| calcium nitrate |  |  |  |  |
| magnesium nitrate |  |  |  |  |
| iron nitrate |  |  |  |  |
| copper nitrate |  |  |  |  |

4 marks

Maximum 4 marks

**END OF TEST**

# Key Stage 3

# Science Test

# Practice Paper 3A

Read this page, but don't open the booklet until your teacher says you can start. Write your name and school in the spaces below.

**First Name** _____

**Last Name** _____

**School** _____

**Remember**

- You have one hour to do the paper.
- Make sure you have these things with you before you start: pen, pencil, rubber, ruler, angle measurer or protractor, calculator.
- The easier questions are at the start of the paper.
- Try to answer all of the questions.
- Don't use any rough paper — write all your answers and working in this test paper.
- Check your work carefully.
- If you're not sure what to do, ask your teacher.

**1.** The diagram shows a circuit containing various different components.
Write the names of the components in the boxes next to their symbols.

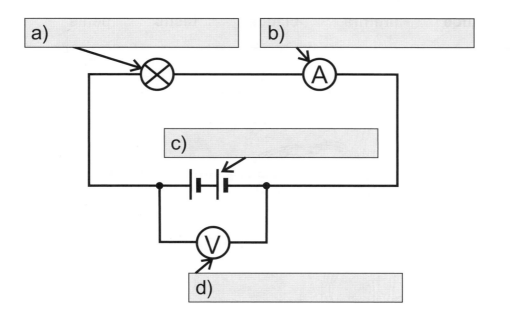

a)

b)

c)

d)

4 marks

Maximum 4 marks

**2.** Draw lines to connect each of the everyday chemicals listed below to the colour it would turn universal indicator, and to its most likely pH value.

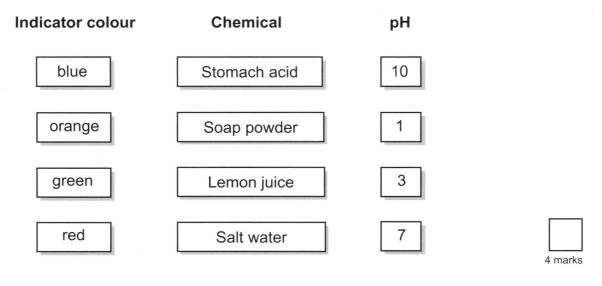

| Indicator colour | Chemical | pH |
| --- | --- | --- |
| blue | Stomach acid | 10 |
| orange | Soap powder | 1 |
| green | Lemon juice | 3 |
| red | Salt water | 7 |

4 marks

Maximum 4 marks

(a)   Choose from the words in the box below to name each part of the male reproductive system labelled on the diagram.

| sperm tube | urethra | bladder | testis | penis |

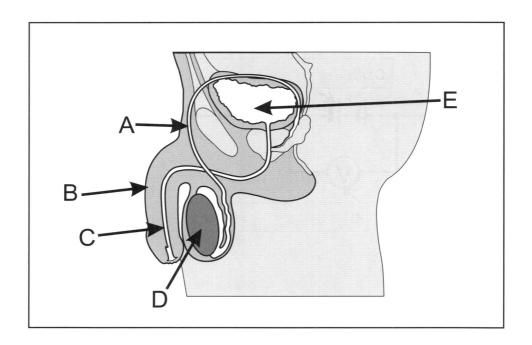

A .............................................................................................................

B .............................................................................................................

C .............................................................................................................

D .............................................................................................................

E .............................................................................................................

4 marks

(b)   Name the sex cell produced by the male reproductive system.

.............................................................................................................

1 mark

Maximum 5 marks

**4.** The picture shows a person ringing a church bell.

The bell is attached upside down to a wheel of radius 1.2 m.
To ring the bell, the rope is pulled.

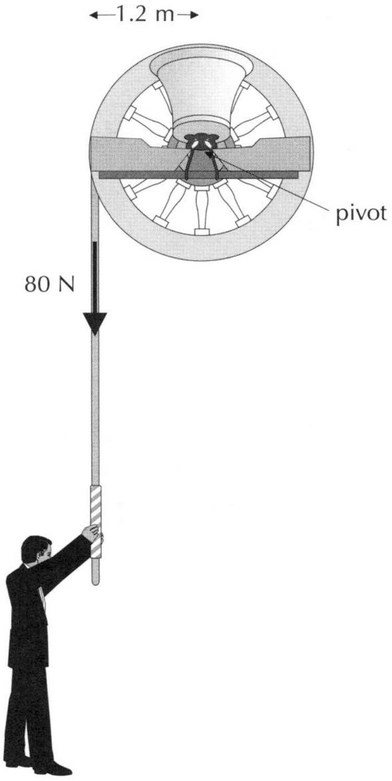

←1.2 m→

80 N

pivot

(a) The bell-ringer pulls on the rope with a downward force of 80 N.
Calculate the moment (turning effect) on the wheel.  Write down the unit.

..............................................................................................................

..............................................................................................................

..............................................................................................................

[ ] 2 marks

(b) The wheel turns as the rope is pulled.  When it is travelling at its highest speed, the rope moves 0.6 m in 0.05 s.  Find the speed.  Write down the unit.

..............................................................................................................

..............................................................................................................

..............................................................................................................

[ ] 2 marks

Continued over the page

(c) Most people can hear the sound of a bell.
Circle the most likely frequency of a bell ringing.

**300 Hz**                    **30 000 Hz**

**3 Hz**          **3 000 000 Hz**

1 mark

(d) Energy is given out when the bell rings. This energy was originally stored in the bell-ringer's body. Describe the sequence of the main energy transfers involved when a person rings a church bell.

.................................................................................................................................

.................................................................................................................................

.................................................................................................................................

.................................................................................................................................

3 marks

Maximum 8 marks

**5.** Yew Fai and Helen investigated the energy values of five different brands of cornflakes using the method shown below. They measured the increase in temperature of the water for each brand of cornflakes.

Their results are shown in the table on the right.

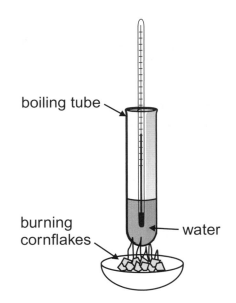

| brand | starting temperature (°C) | final temperature (°C) | temperature change (°C) |
|---|---|---|---|
| A | 21 | 41 | |
| B | 19 | 43 | |
| C | 20 | 49 | |
| D | 21 | 42 | |
| E | 22 | 50 | |

(a) Fill in the temperature change (°C) column of the table.

2 marks

(b) Give two things that Yew Fai and Helen needed to do to make this a fair test.

1. ............................................................................................................

2. ............................................................................................................

2 marks

(c) What could they do to improve the reliability of their results?

....................................................................................................................

1 mark

(d) Suggest one change they could make to their apparatus to improve the accuracy of the results.

....................................................................................................................

1 mark

Maximum 6 marks

**6.** Wine is about 10% alcohol and 90% water. The table shows some information about water and alcohol, and the diagram shows the equipment used to turn wine into brandy.

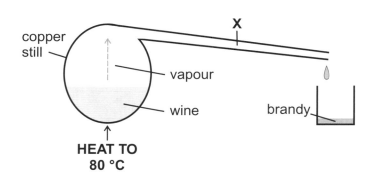

| Substance | Boiling Temp. |
| --- | --- |
| Water | 100 °C |
| Alcohol | 78 °C |

(a) What is the name of this separation process?

.................................................................................................

1 mark

(b) Why can you separate water and alcohol using this process?

.................................................................................................

1 mark

(c) What process is taking place at point X on the diagram?

.................................................................................................

1 mark

(d) Which do you think contains a greater percentage of alcohol, wine or brandy? Explain how you can tell from the method shown above.

.................................................................................................

.................................................................................................

.................................................................................................

2 marks

Maximum 5 marks

**7.** An igneous rock, for example granite, can become a sedimentary rock.
A model of the process was carried out in a school laboratory as shown below.

**Stage 1**

Fill a plastic container half way with pieces of granite, and cover with dilute acid. Leave for seven days, then pour off the acid.

**Stage 2**

Shake the container for a few minutes.

**Stage 3**

Pour the contents of the container through a sieve, into a dish of sea water.

sieve

fine material

sea water

**Stage 4**

Leave to stand for 3-4 hours.

**Stage 5**

Place heavy weights to press the wet, fine material for several weeks.

(a) Chemical weathering in the rock cycle is shown in Stage 1. Which part of the rock cycle does Stage 2 show?

.........................................

.........................................

☐ 1 mark

(b) Pieces of granite are carried from a mountain to the sea. The pieces of granite change as they are carried. Describe two ways they change.

1. .................................................

.................................................

.................................................

.................................................

2. .................................................

.................................................

.................................................

.................................................

☐ 2 marks

(c) Stages 4 and 5 represent parts of the rock cycle. Which two parts do they represent?

Stage 4:

.........................................

.........................................

☐ 1 mark

Stage 5:

.........................................

.........................................

☐ 1 mark

Maximum 5 marks

**8.** Mr Grey likes making toast in front of his open fire.

(a) He made his toasting fork himself. He had a choice of these materials:

| copper | steel | plastic | wood |

Suggest a good choice of material for:

(i) The handle. ...............................................

Give a reason for your choice.

..................................................................................................

2 marks

(ii) The prongs. ...............................................

Give a reason for your choice.

..................................................................................................

2 marks

(b) Smoke from his fire always goes up the chimney.
Explain why this happens.

..................................................................................................

..................................................................................................

1 mark

(c) Explain how heat gets from the fire to the slice of toast.

..................................................................................................

..................................................................................................

1 mark

Maximum 6 marks

**9.** Libby investigated the chemical reaction between sulfur powder and iron filings. She mixed them together in a crucible and heated them strongly in a Bunsen flame for five minutes.

She recorded her observations in the table below.

| Substance | Description | Appearance | Magnetic? |
|---|---|---|---|
| 1 | Iron filings | Grey filings | Yes |
| 2 | Sulfur powder | Yellow powder | No |
| 3 | Mixture | Yellow and grey powder | Grey bits only |
| 4 | Final product | Shiny black solid | No |

(a)    Write down one safety precaution Libby will need to take in this investigation.

    ......................................................................................................................

1 mark

(b)    Write down the substance number of one element and one compound from the table above.

    Element:    ................        Compound:    ................

2 marks

(c)    (i)    Write down the **name** of the substance produced in the chemical reaction.

        ..........................................................................................................

1 mark

    (ii)    When iron (Fe) and sulfur (S) atoms join together, one atom of iron combines with one atom of sulfur.
        Write down the **chemical formula** of the substance produced.

        ..........................................................................................................

1 mark

(d)    Libby began the experiment with 5.6 g iron and reacted it all with sulfur.
    Tick the box you think is the most likely mass of the product.

    ☐ 5.6 g        ☐ 2.8 g        ☐ 8.8 g        ☐ 1.0 g

1 mark

Maximum 6 marks

**10.** A candle burns under a glass jar.

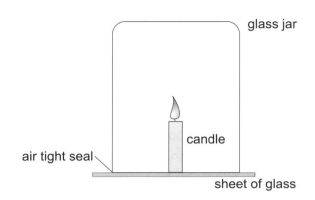

(a)　(i)　There is a reaction when the candle burns.
　　　　Give the chemical formulae of two of the products of this reaction.

　　　　1. ...............................................................................................

　　　　2. ...............................................................................................

　　　　　　　　　　　　　　　　　　　　　　　　　　　　　　　　2 marks

　　(ii)　What could you see to show that a chemical reaction
　　　　is taking place?　Give two examples.

　　　　1. ...............................................................................................

　　　　...............................................................................................

　　　　2. ...............................................................................................

　　　　...............................................................................................

　　　　　　　　　　　　　　　　　　　　　　　　　　　　　　　　2 marks

(b)    The candle is replaced with a pot plant.

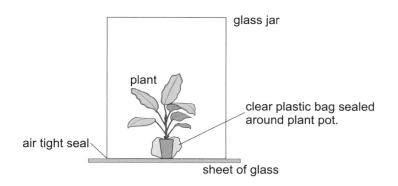

(i)    What effect does the plant's photosynthesis have on
the levels of different gases in the jar?

1. ....................................................................................

2. ....................................................................................

2 marks

(ii)   If you covered the jar with a black bag, what effect
would this have on these changes?

....................................................................................

....................................................................................

....................................................................................

2 marks

(c)    Plants need chlorophyll to photosynthesise.

(i)    Which part of the cell contains chlorophyll?

....................................................................................

1 mark

(ii)   Which part of the cell controls chlorophyll production?

....................................................................................

1 mark

Maximum 10 marks

**11.** Wind power can be used to generate electricity using wind turbines like the one below.

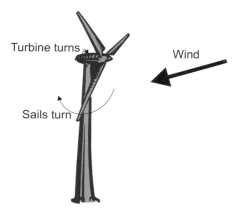

Turbine turns

Wind

Sails turn

(a)  As the wind spins the sails of the wind turbine, it turns a generator, which produces electricity.
Describe the useful energy changes which take place in this process.

........................................................................................................

........................................................................................................

........................................................................................................

........................................................................................................

2 marks

(b)  Explain why wind is called a renewable energy source.

........................................................................................................

........................................................................................................

1 mark

(c)  Give one further examples of renewable energy source that can be used to generate electricity.

........................................................................................................

1 marks

Maximum 4 marks

**12.** The diagram below shows a food web.

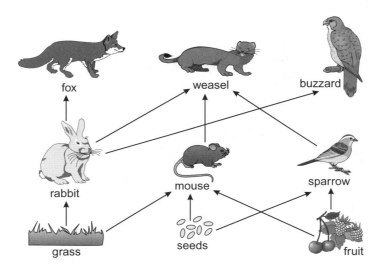

(a) Name two primary consumers from this food web.

...................................................................................................

2 marks

(b) Name two secondary consumers from this food web.

...................................................................................................

2 marks

(c) What is the source of energy for all food webs?

...................................................................................................

1 mark

(d) If all the rabbits were killed by a disease, what do you think would happen to the populations of the following animals? Give a reason for your answer in each case.

(i) the weasels?

...................................................................................................

...................................................................................................

1 mark

(ii) the mice?

...................................................................................................

...................................................................................................

1 mark

Maximum 7 marks

**13.** Mrs Lightfoot and her elephant walk across a wooden floor.
Mrs Lightfoot's high heels leave marks on the floor.  The elephant's feet do not.

The elephant has a mass of 3000 kg.  Mrs Lightfoot has a mass of 50 kg.

Explain why Mrs Lightfoot's heels mark the floor
but the elephant does no damage.

..................................................................................................................................

..................................................................................................................................

2 marks

Maximum 2 marks

**14.** Sid makes a stack of 800 kg of bricks on top of a board.
The board has an area of 0.25 square metres.

(a)     Work out the weight of the bricks in newtons (g = 10 N/kg).

..................................................................................................................................

1 mark

(b)     Calculate the pressure under the board.

..................................................................................................................................

..................................................................................................................................

..................................................................................................................................

2 marks

Maximum 3 marks

**END OF TEST**

# Key Stage 3

## Science Test

# Practice Paper 3B

Science

KEY STAGE
3

PRACTICE PAPER
3B

Read this page, but don't open the booklet until your teacher says you can start. Write your name and school in the spaces below.

**First Name** _____

**Last Name** _____

**School** _____

**Remember**

■ You have one hour to do the paper.

■ Make sure you have these things with you before you start: pen, pencil, rubber, ruler, angle measurer or protractor, calculator.

■ The easier questions are at the start of the paper.

■ Try to answer all of the questions.

■ Don't use any rough paper — write all your answers and working in this test paper.

■ Check your work carefully.

■ If you're not sure what to do, ask your teacher.

**1.** Some friends are having a tug of war. The diagram shows the two teams and the force with which each person is pulling.

27 N   24 N   21 N                     19 N   32 N   23 N

TEAM A                                      TEAM B

Which team will win, if each person pulls with a constant force?
Show your working.

................................................................................................................

................................................................................................................

................................................................................................................

3 marks

Maximum 3 marks

**2.** Alcohol is a recreational drug.

(a) Which one of these properties makes alcohol a **drug**?
Circle the correct answer.

**It's a chemical.**

**It can provide energy.**

**It's soluble in water.**

**It affects the nervous system.**

1 mark

(b) Look at this graph:

(i) Use the graph to describe how an increase in the amount of alcohol in the blood affects a person's chance of having an accident.

.........................................................................................................

.........................................................................................................

.........................................................................................................

2 marks

(ii) Which of the following could explain why alcohol in the blood could cause accidents? Circle the correct answer.

**Alcohol lowers body temperature.**

**Alcohol is a stimulant.**

**Alcohol increases the time it takes for a person to react.**

**Alcohol makes people happy.**

1 mark

Maximum 4 marks

**3.** The diagram shows a sketch of a cell from a rabbit as seen down a powerful microscope.

(a)   Label the diagram:

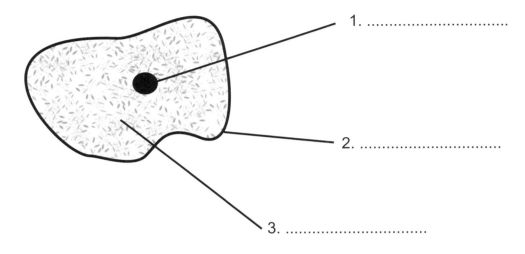

1. ..................................

2. ..................................

3. ..................................

$\boxed{\phantom{xx}}$
3 marks

(b)   Name two parts which would be found in a plant cell and not in an animal one.

1. ....................................................................................................

2. ....................................................................................................

$\boxed{\phantom{xx}}$
2 marks

(c)   The cell is one of a group of similar cells working together.
What is such a group of similar cells called?

....................................................................................................

$\boxed{\phantom{xx}}$
1 mark

Maximum 6 marks

**4.** Use the information in the table below to answer the questions that follow.

| SUBSTANCE | CHEMICAL FORMULA |
|---|---|
| water | $H_2O$ |
| carbon dioxide | $CO_2$ |
| alcohol (ethanol) | $C_2H_5OH$ |
| glucose | $C_6H_{12}O_6$ |
| oxygen | $O_2$ |

(a)   Which substance is an element?

.................................................................................................... ☐

1 mark

(b)   Which element is present in all the substances?

.................................................................................................... ☐

1 mark

(c)   How many atoms are there in one molecule of glucose?

.................................................................................................... ☐

1 mark

Maximum 3 marks

**5.** Wayne is investigating friction in liquids. He times how long it takes a marble to fall through a tube filled with wallpaper paste.

Here are his results:

| Distance fallen by marble (cm) | Time taken (s) |
|---|---|
| 10 | 2.1 |
| 20 | 4.3 |
| 30 | 6.0 |
| 40 | 8.4 |
| 50 | 9.9 |

(a) Use the blank graph paper below to draw a graph of Wayne's results. Draw a line of best fit.

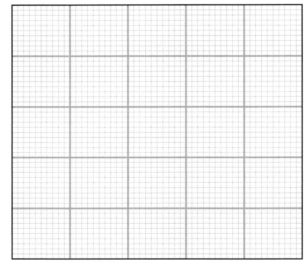

Distance fallen by marble (cm)

Time taken (s)

3 marks

(b) What do his results tell Wayne about the speed of the falling marble?

.................................................................................................................

.................................................................................................................

1 mark

Maximum 4 marks

**6.** A general equation for a neutralisation reaction is:

**acid + alkali → a salt + water**

(a)  Draw lines to connect each of the salts below to the acid
     and the alkali that would react to form them.

| Acid | Salt | Alkali |
|------|------|--------|
| hydrochloric acid | calcium chloride | copper hydroxide |
| sulfuric acid | iron nitrate | calcium hydroxide |
| nitric acid | copper sulfate | iron hydroxide |

3 marks

(b)  Complete the word equation for the following neutralisation reaction:

sodium
hydroxide  +  .................................  →  sodium
chloride  +  water

1 mark

(c)  Write down the name of the acid that has the chemical formula: $HNO_3$.

.............................................................................................

1 mark

Maximum 5 marks

**7.** Matt uses a pump to inflate a balloon.
He notices that the pump gets hot as he uses it.

(a) How and where was the energy stored before it was transferred to pump up the balloon?

........................................................................................................

2 marks

(b) Explain how the gas molecules inside the balloon exert pressure on the walls of the balloon.

........................................................................................................

........................................................................................................

1 mark

(c) The air going into the balloon is warmed up by the pumping.
How will this affect the motion of the gas molecules inside the balloon?

........................................................................................................

........................................................................................................

1 mark

(d) As the air in the balloon becomes hotter, the pressure rises. Write down one reason, in terms of the motion of gas molecules, why the pressure rises.

........................................................................................................

........................................................................................................

1 mark

Maximum 5 marks

**8.** Methane is a gas. A molecule of methane consists of one carbon atom chemically joined to four hydrogen atoms.

(a) Write a word equation for the reaction that happens when methane burns in air.

..................................................................................................................... ☐

2 marks

(b) If pure methane is burnt in a closed container, how will the air inside the container be different afterwards? Tick any answers that apply.
The air inside the container will contain:

☐ More hydrogen                    ☐ More oxygen

☐ More carbon dioxide              ☐ More sulfur dioxide

☐ Less hydrogen                    ☐ Less oxygen

☐ Less carbon dioxide              ☐ Less sulfur dioxide        ☐

2 marks

(c) When methane was burnt in a closed container, carbon (soot) and carbon monoxide were formed, as well as the usual products.
Which of the following is the best explanation for this?

A    The methane burned too quickly.

B    The air inside the container was too damp.

C    There was not enough oxygen for the methane to burn completely.

D    The methane contained impurities.

Answer:     ................                ☐

1 mark

Maximum 5 marks

9. The diagram shows a plank pivoted at one end.
A force of 100 N pushes up on the plank.

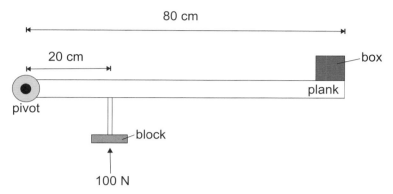

(a) Calculate the moment (turning affect) of the 100 N force about the pivot.
Show your working.

...................................................................................................................................

...................................................................................................................................

3 marks

(b) The box is on the right hand end of the plank.
It is just heavy enough to keep the plank balanced.

(i) What is the moment of the box about the pivot? Give the units.

...........................................................................................................................

1 mark

(ii) What is the weight of the box?

...........................................................................................................................

1 mark

(iii) The 100 N force acts on a block with area 5 cm².
Calculate the pressure on the block. Give the units.

...........................................................................................................................

...........................................................................................................................

...........................................................................................................................

...........................................................................................................................

2 marks

Maximum 7 marks

**10.** Tony is carrying out an experiment to compare the rate of photosynthesis of two types of algae. The following diagram shows the reaction that happens.

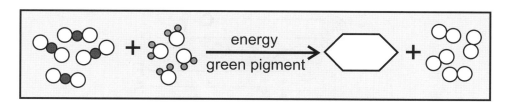

(a) Write out the word equation for this reaction.

..................................................................................................................................

1 mark

The diagram shows the equipment Tony is using for the experiment.

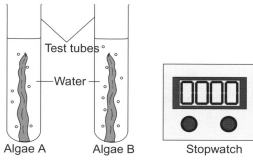

(b) How can Tony use this equipment to measure the rate of photosynthesis?

..................................................................................................................................

1 mark

(c) What can Tony do to make his results reliable?

..................................................................................................................................

1 mark

(d) Name the green pigment needed for photosynthesis to happen.

..................................................................................................................................

1 mark

(e) What type of energy is used to drive this reaction?

..................................................................................................................................

1 mark

Maximum 5 marks

**11.** The diagram shows the human female reproductive system.

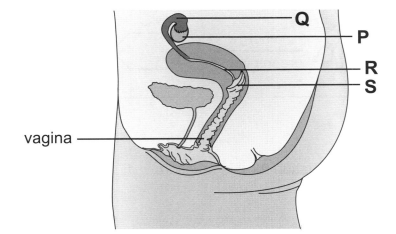

vagina

(a) Give the correct labels for the structures P, Q, R and S.

P ........................................... Q ...............................................

R ........................................... S ...............................................

4 marks

(b) From which part are the ova or eggs released at ovulation?

..............................................................................................................

1 mark

(c) On approximately which day in the menstrual cycle does ovulation occur (if day one is when menstruation begins)?

..............................................................................................................

1 mark

(d) Explain how the uterus changes each month to prepare for a fertilised egg.

..............................................................................................................

1 mark

Maximum 7 marks

**12.** In an experiment, a ray of sunlight was directed onto a triangular prism made out of glass, as shown below.

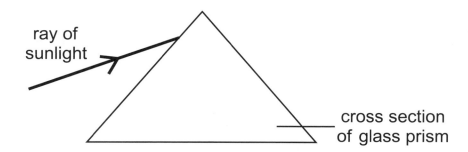

(a)   Complete the diagram to show what happens to the ray of light.

[  ]

3 marks

(b)   Which of the following words correctly describe what happens to the ray of light?  Tick **two** boxes.

[  ] absorption

[  ] dispersion

[  ] refraction

[  ] radiation

[  ]

2 marks

Maximum 5 marks

**13.** A teacher shows her class two different experiments. She pushes a metal coin through a slot into a money box.

Next, she takes the coin out and heats it strongly. She tries to put the heated coin into the money box, but it won't fit through the slot.

In her second experiment, the teacher stands at the end of the classroom and opens a bottle of rose-water. It takes about a minute for everyone in the class to smell the rose-water. After lunch she does the same thing, but this time she warms the bottle slightly before opening it. This time it only takes half as long for everyone to smell the perfume.

(a) Explain, in terms of the particles in the coin, why the heated coin won't fit through the slot.

..........................................................................................................

..........................................................................................................

..........................................................................................................

2 marks

(b) Explain, in terms of particles, why the class smelled the rose-water more quickly when it had been warmed.

..........................................................................................................

..........................................................................................................

..........................................................................................................

2 marks

(c) What do both of your explanations have in common?

..........................................................................................................

..........................................................................................................

2 marks

Maximum 6 marks

**14.** Look at this circuit diagram.

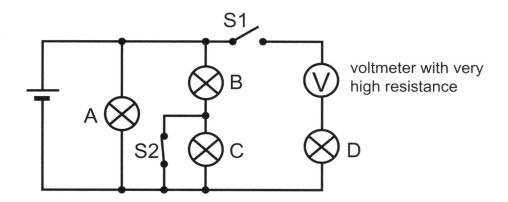

There are four bulbs, **A**, **B**, **C** and **D**, in the circuit.

(a)    In the spaces below, state which bulbs are lit and which are not lit when
switch S1 is open and S2 is closed as shown above.

Lit bulbs .................................................................................................

Unlit bulbs ..............................................................................................

2 marks

(b)    What three changes should be made to the circuit shown above to
make sure all the bulbs are lit?

1. .......................................................................................................

2. .......................................................................................................

3. .......................................................................................................

3 marks

Maximum 5 marks

**15.** Potassium chloride is a white, crystalline solid at room temperature. Tim and Sarah are carrying out an experiment to see what happens when they mix potassium chloride crystals (KCl) with water. They add some KCl crystals to a beaker of water and stir it.

Tim says the KCl disappears because it is no longer in the water.
Sarah says the KCl disappears because it has dissolved in the water.

(a) Suggest how Tim and Sarah could test their explanations to find out who is right.

..................................................................................................................

..................................................................................................................

☐ 2 marks

Sarah suggests testing their explanations by putting a piece of magnesium into the beaker. She says that the potassium will leave a deposit on the magnesium as they react. They try this, but there is no reaction.

Tim says the lack of a reaction proves there was no KCl in the solution.
Sarah is confused because her textbook says that KCl dissolves in water.

(b) Use the data below to explain why Tim is wrong.

..................................................................................................................

☐ 1 mark

Reactivity Series

Potassium
Sodium
Calcium
Magnesium
Aluminium

(c) Would it be better for Sarah and Tim to rely on their first-hand experience or a secondary source? Give a reason for your answer.

..................................................................................................................

..................................................................................................................

☐ 2 marks

Maximum 5 marks

**END OF TEST**

# Answers

## KS3 Science Paper 1A

| Q | Marks | Correct answer | Useful tips |
|---|---|---|---|
| **1.** a | 3 | Carbon compounds in fossil fuels like coal, oil and natural gas - C. Decomposers release carbon dioxide into the air - A. Photosynthesis by plants - B. **One mark for each.** | |
| b | 1 | Combustion/Burning. | |
| **2.** a | 1 | The amount / volume / mass / weight of the tea / water used. | |
| b | 1 | The temperature of the tea. | |
| c | 1 | Initial temperature **OR** size / shape of cup **OR** material cup was made from / amount of insulation **OR** time Tim left the cups of tea for **OR** where the cups were left. | |
| **3.** a i | 1 | Solid — C. | |
| ii | 1 | Melting — D. | |
| iii | 1 | Condensing — F. | *Tip: Subliming, as you might have gathered, is where a substance turns straight from a solid into a gas (or vice versa) without going through the liquid stage. Not many substances do it and you don't really need to know much about it, so don't worry about it too much.* |
| iv | 1 | Liquid — A. | |
| v | 1 | Freezing — G. | |
| vi | 1 | Gas — B. | |
| vii | 1 | Boiling — E. | |
| b | 1 | Condensing (F) **OR** Freezing (G) | |
| **4.** a | 2 | Light from the lamp shines on the cup and is scattered **OR** reflected. **One mark.** Some of the light travels to Suzanne's eyes and she sees the cup. **One mark.** | |
| b | 2 | **The blank boxes of the table should read, 'red — blue' One mark for each.** | |
| c | 1 | Black absorbs all light. **OR** It doesn't scatter any light. | |
| d i | 1 | 30° | |
| ii | 1 | 30° | |
| iii | 1 | 2.5 cm | *TIP: Make sure you measure this perpendicular to the mirror — not along the light rays.* |
| iv | 1 | 2.5 cm | |
| **5.** a | 3 | Zinc — zinc nitrate — nitric acid [**One mark**]. Iron — iron sulfate — sulfuric acid [**One mark**]. Lead — lead chloride — hydrochloric acid [**One mark**]. | |
| b i | 1 | E.g. Universal indicator solution [**One mark**]. | |
| ii | 1 | E.g. The solution would turn red or orange [**One mark**]. | *Tip: All acids contain hydrogen. Metals like zinc, iron and lead, on the other hand, are pure elements. The only atoms they contain are the metal atoms.* |
| c | 1 | The acid. | |
| **6.** a | 3 | A — cell wall [**One mark**]. B — chloroplast [**One mark**]. C — vacuole [**One mark**]. | |
| b | 1 | To support the cell. | *Tip: Never make the mistake of thinking that all plant cells have chloroplasts. There's not much point unless the cell photosynthesises, now is there?* |
| c | 2 | Roots are found underground where there is no light [**One mark**]. They don't need chloroplasts as they don't photosynthesise [**One mark**]. | |
| **7.** a | 2 | $40 \times 0.5 = 20$ Nm (2000 Ncm) **One mark for answer without unit.** | |
| b | 1 | $20 \div 0.2 = 100$ N **Accept answer to (a) $\div$ 0.2.** | |
| c | 2 | $0.5$ cm$^2$ = $0.5 \div 10\,000$ m$^2$, P = F / A = $80 / 0.00005 = 1\,600\,000$ Pa or Nm$^{-2}$ [**One mark for answer without unit.**] **OR** P = $80 \div 0.5 = 160$ Ncm$^{-2}$ [**One mark.**] | |
| **8.** a | 2 | Potassium, zinc, nickel, platinum. **(One mark for getting zinc and nickel the wrong way round).** | |
| b | 1 | Sodium | |
| c i | 1 | Platinum | *TIP: Bleugh, reactivity series. This is <u>hard</u> but you've <u>got</u> to learn it.* |
| ii | 1 | Zinc is less reactive than potassium so it does not replace it in the salt. | |

| 9. | a | 2 | It damages the cilia, leading to smoker's cough/bronchitis/emphysema **[One mark]**. It contains carcinogens which cause lung cancer **[One mark]**. |
|---|---|---|---|
| | b | 3 | <br><br>*Tip: If you're asked to do a graph and you have to come up with the scales for the axes yourself, the rule is that you use as much of the available space as you can. Try not to end up with a tiny graph cramped in one corner of the graph paper. Having said that, it's even more important you pick a sensible scale — don't have each small square being worth 3.25 units or anything silly like that.*<br><br>**[One mark for labelling the axes correctly, one mark for both scales shown correctly on the axes, one mark for showing each bar with the correct height]** |
| | c | 1 | Smoking increases the risk of the baby having a smaller birth mass, which can lead to health problems. |

| 10. | a i | 1 | Photosynthesis |
|---|---|---|---|
| | ii | 1 | Oxygen |
| | iii | 1 | Carbon dioxide |
| | iv | 1 | Respiration |
| | b | 2 | There are no insects or other animals to transfer pollen.<br>There is no wind to transfer pollen. **One mark for each.** |

| 11. | a | 1 | There was a bright flame **OR** ash formed **OR** the magnesium metal turned into white powder. |
|---|---|---|---|
| | b | 1 | Magnesium oxide. |
| | c | 1 | Magnesium + oxygen → magnesium oxide. |

| 12. | a | 1 | A mixture of compounds. |
|---|---|---|---|
| | b i | 1 | It is a gas. |
| | ii | 1 | Cold water flowing through the condenser cools the naphtha, so it turns back into a liquid. |

| 13. | a | 3 | <br><br>**[One mark for correctly plotting all the points, one mark for labelling the axes correctly, one mark for a smooth curve through the points similar to that shown]** |
|---|---|---|---|
| | b | 2 | The rate of photosynthesis / amount of gas/oxygen produced is lower **[One mark]** the further the lamp is from the plant / the lower the light intensity is **[One mark]**. |

| 14. | a i | 1 | |
|---|---|---|---|
| | ii | 1 | |
| | b | 1 | |
| | c i | 1 | Accept 1.7 - 1.9 **[One mark]** |
| | ii | 1 | Accept 33 - 35 **[One mark]** |
| | d | 1 | As the length of the wire increases, the resistance increases **[One mark]**. |

# KS3 Science Paper 1B

| Q | Marks | Correct answer | Useful tips |
|---|---|---|---|

**1.** a i — 1 — Water.

ii — 1 — Syrup.

iii — 1 — Sugar.

b — 1 — Heat the mixture **OR** stir the mixture.

*Tip: When something dissolves, it hasn't disappeared — its particles have just got so spread out among the particles of solvent that you can't see them any more. So anything that helps them spread out, like stirring or giving them more energy, will help them dissolve.*

---

**2.** — 5 — Small intestine — absorbs nutrients into the bloodstream [One mark]. Stomach — churns up food and mixes it with acid and enzymes [One mark]. Teeth — grind up food and mix it with saliva [One mark]. Large intestine — absorbs water from the food waste [One mark]. Gullet — moves food to the next part of the digestive system by peristalsis [One mark].

---

**3.** — 3 —

| Description | Letter |
|---|---|
| An element made up of molecules | B |
| Molecules in a compound | C |
| A mixture of different elements | D |
| An element made up of atoms | A |

[Three marks for all correct, one mark for two correct, two marks for three correct]

*Tip: If you're still getting mixed up with atoms and compounds and elements and molecules, now's the time to get it all worked out. Molecules are made from more than one atom joined together, and they can be elements (if both atoms are the same) or compounds (if the atoms are of different elements).*

---

**4.** a i — 1 — Larger than the drag. *[The forward force must be more to make the bike speed up.]*

ii — 1 — Equal to the drag. *[The movement is staying the same so the forces are balanced.]*

iii — 1 — Less than the drag. *[The drag must be more to slow the bike down.]*

b — 1 — Friction

---

**5.** a — 2 — Gas A — oxygen [One mark]. Gas B — carbon dioxide [One mark].

b — 1 — Respiration.

c — 1 — glucose + oxygen $\rightarrow$ carbon dioxide + water (+ energy).

---

**6.** a — 1 — potassium nitrate

b — 1 — sodium sulfate

c — 1 — calcium chloride

*Tip: You need to take the first half of the name of the alkali, and put it with the first half of the name of the acid.*

---

**7.** a — 2 — Use the same weight of crisps and snack **OR** Use the same amount of; and starting temperature of; water **OR** Keep the same distance of crisp or snack to the test tube. **One mark for any of these up to 2 marks.**

b — 2 — Wear goggles **OR** Point the test tube away from him **OR** Light the food at arms length. **One mark for any 2.**

c — 1 — A. *Because they have a higher energy content.*

d — 1 — Oranges **OR** peas **OR** beans **OR** lemons *Other answers possible.* **One mark for any one of these.**

e i — 1 — Provides a hard substance to clean out the digestive system.

ii — 2 — Lower in fat. Higher in fibre. **One mark for each.**

---

**8.** a — 1 — B.

b — 1 — A.

c — 1 — D.

d — 1 — E.

e — 1 — C.

*Tip: There's no excuse for mixing up the rock types. Sedimentary rocks are made from sediments — little crumbs of old rock and dead matter that gradually build up into new rock. Metamorphic rocks have metamorphosised (the fancy word for changed) from one type to another. Then all that's left to remember are igneous rocks — they're the, erm, interesting ones, made from volcanoes and lava and stuff.*

---

**9.** a — 2 — copper sulfate + magnesium $\rightarrow$ magnesium sulfate + copper [Lose one mark for each mistake].

b — 1 — Because the magnesium takes the place of the copper in the copper sulfate solution, forcing the copper out.

c — 1 — Magnesium. *Tip: Don't get confused — the more reactive element would never be left sitting on its own as a pure metal.*

---

*Answers*

| 10. | a | 2 | When it's summer in England the northern half of the Earth is tilted towards the Sun [One mark], so as the Earth turns, the Sun's rays reach it for more of the day [One mark]. |
| | b | 2 | Because the Sun's rays are spread over a small area of land [One mark] so the heat is focused on a small area and the land gets warm [One mark]. |

| 11. | a | 1 | The concentration of the acid [One mark]. |
| | b | 2 | Any two of: the volume of acid / mass of marble chips / the size/surface area of the marble chips [Two marks]. |
| | c | 1 | Repeat her experiment and take an average of the results [One mark]. |
| | d i | 3 | [One mark for numbering and labelling the axes correctly, one mark for plotting the points correctly, one mark for joining the points with a smooth curve] |
| | ii | 1 | E.g. the mass of the beaker and contents decreases for 20 minutes and then stays the same [One mark]. |
| | iii | 1 | 18½ minutes. *The mass was still changing after 15 minutes, but had stopped by 20, meaning the reaction had finished.* |
| | iv | 2 | 250.0 − 239.5 = 10.5 g. [One mark for correct answer, one mark for correct unit] |

| 12. | a | 2 | If only red and blue light shine on the dress, it absorbs the blue light [One mark] and reflects only the red light and so appears red [One mark]. |
| | b | 2 | Yellow light is made up of red and green light [One mark]. When both red and green light are shining on it, the dress reflects both colours and appears yellow [One mark]. |
| | c | 1 | Yellow. |

| 13. | a | 2 | One muscle contracts to bend the joint [One mark] and the other contracts to straighten the joint [One mark]. |
| | b | 1 | A |

| 14. | a | 1 | The arrow should be drawn pointing directly upwards from the sliding bolt, towards the electromagnet. |
| | b | 1 | Gravity. |
| | c | 1 | iron **OR** steel **OR** nickel **OR** cobalt. |
| | d | 1 | Use a higher voltage/current/more powerful battery **OR** have more turns in the coil of wire of the electromagnet **OR** use a better (more easily magnetised) material for the core of the electromagnet. |

| 15. | a | 3 | [Take away one mark for each mistake or omission] |
| | b | 1 | There are many variables that cannot be controlled when working in the field [One mark]. |
| | c | 1 | By counting the number of slugs and snails using a quadrat. [One mark] |
| | d | 2 | The number of blue tits will decrease [One mark], as there will be less food/fewer slugs and snails for them [One mark]. |

# KS3 Science Paper 2A

| Q | Marks | Correct answer | Useful tips |
|---|---|---|---|
| 1. | 3 | Muscle — tissue [One mark].  Heart **AND** Brain — organ [One mark]. <br> Sperm **AND** Neurone — cell [One mark]. | |
| 2. a | 4 | A — stomach, B — large intestine **OR** colon, C — small intestine, D — anus **OR** rectum <br> **[One mark for each correct answer].** | |
| b | 1 | Many food molecules are too big to be absorbed into the bloodstream/can't pass through the gut wall. | |
| 3. a | 1 | Sedimentary | |
| b | 1 | Metamorphic | |
| c | 1 | Igneous | |
| 4. a | 1 | DNA | |
| b | 1 | Sperm. | |
| c | 1 | Nuclei **OR** Nucleus **OR** Chromosomes | |
| d | 1 | Inherit. | |
| 5. a | 1 | Distillation | |
| b | 1 | 100 °C | |
| c | 1 | It condenses the water vapour. | |
| d | 4 | **1** Condensing  **2** Boiling **OR** Evaporating  **3** Melting  **4** Freezing | |
| e | 1 | *in piece of apparatus labelled X* 1   *in the flask containing impure water* 2   **Both required for one mark.** | |

| 6. a | 1 | conduction | |
|---|---|---|---|
| b | 3 | Your graph should look similar to → | **[One mark for a sensible scale and correctly-labelled axes, one mark for correctly plotting all the points, one mark for good line of best fit.]** |
| c | 2 | She could use metal blocks made of different metals (but of the same mass) [One mark].  She would need to calculate the change in temperature over time [One mark]. | |
| d | 1 | Accept 55 °C - 57 °C. | |
| e | 1 | It is easier to see the trend. | |

| 7. a | 1 | The ice melted. | *Tip: So, kinetic energy. Sounds a bit technical, but it's simple really. All particles move about a bit — even in solids they vibrate, and in gases they rush about like crazy. When something warms up, the kinetic energy of its particles increases.  When something cools down, the kinetic energy of its particles decreases.  That's why solids tend to be quite stiff and dense, and gases are floaty and, well, mainly empty space.* |
|---|---|---|---|
| b | 1 | Their kinetic energy increased. | |
| c | 1 | Their kinetic energy decreased. | |
| d | 1 | 10 °C | |
| e | 1 | 20 °C | |

| 8. a | 1 | kinetic | |
|---|---|---|---|
| b | 1 | The wind energy is free **OR** it causes less environmental problems/pollution than electricity produced by burning fossil fuels **OR** it uses a renewable energy resource. | |
| c | 1 | Any one of: it's less reliable because the wind doesn't always blow, it spoils the view, it is noisy, there is a low energy output, it is expensive to build. | |
| d | 1 | The Sun. | |

*Answers*

| 9. | a | 1 | A and Y |
|---|---|---|---|
| | b | 1 | It is made of a mixture of substance A or Y and substance B. |
| | c | 1 | An ink line would be separated out by the solvent and make the chromatogram unclear. |
| | d | 1 | If it was below the surface the substances would wash out into the solvent instead of moving up the paper. |

| 10. | a | i | 1 | 20 kWh |
|---|---|---|---|---|
| | | ii | 1 | 240p OR £2.40 |
| | b | i | 1 | 0.3 kWh |
| | | ii | 1 | 3.5 hours |

| 11. | a | 3 | E.g. |
|---|---|---|---|
| | | | [Circuit complete for one mark, lamps connected in parallel for one mark, switches to isolate the lamps independently for one mark.] |
| | b | 2 | The battery might run out more quickly / need replacing more often [One mark] because more energy would be needed to power both the lamps [One mark]. |

| 12. | a | 1 | magnesium + water $\rightarrow$ magnesium oxide + hydrogen |
|---|---|---|---|
| | b | i | 2 | potassium + water $\rightarrow$ potassium hydroxide [One mark] + hydrogen [One mark]. |
| | | ii | 1 | alkali |
| | | ii | 1 | pH 12 |

| 13. | a | 1 | Filtration |
|---|---|---|---|
| | b | 1 | As a control OR To show it's the dissolved substances that affect it |
| | c | i | 1 | Minerals OR salts OR nutrients |
| | | ii | 1 | Root hairs OR Large surface area OR They spread out |
| | d | 1 | The leaves need light for photosynthesis. |

| 14. | a | 1 | A |
|---|---|---|---|
| | b | 1 | C |
| | c | 1 | B     Tip: Remember, air resistance isn't a fixed thing. It changes depending on how fast you're going and how big you are. |
| | d | 1 | C |
| | e | 2 | speed = distance ÷ time = 100 ÷ 15 = 6.7 m/s [Correct answer for one mark, correct unit for one mark.] |

| 15. | a | 2 | Tablet B [One mark]. Because it neutralised more acid than tablet A [One mark]. |
|---|---|---|---|
| | b | 2 | Any two of: e.g. strength/concentration of acid / volume of drops / temperature [One mark each]. |
| | c | 1 | Type of tablet |
| | d | 1 | He could repeat the experiment and calculate an average. |

*Answers*

104

# KS3 Science Paper 2B

| Q | Marks | Correct answer | Useful tips |
|---|---|---|---|
| **1.** a | 3 | Copper — 1 [One mark]. Sulfur — 1 [One mark]. Oxygen — 4 [One mark]. | |
| b | 1 | Copper sulfate.   *Tip: If you've recognised the copper, the sulfur and the oxygen, the name of the salt should be pretty obvious.* | |

**2.** a | 2 | E.g.

[One mark for a straight line from any point on the child to the mirror, a straight line from the top mirror to the bottom mirror and a straight line from the mirror to the driver's eye, one mark for direction of light going from child to driver.]

*Tip: Of course, there are other rays of light bouncing off every bit of the child he can see. Luckily you only have to show one of them — otherwise things would get very complicated.*

b | 2 |

light ray

reflector

[One mark for showing that the light is reflected onto the opposite surface. One mark for showing that it is then reflected back in the direction from which it originally came.]

| Q | Marks | Correct answer | Useful tips |
|---|---|---|---|
| **3.** a | 2 | Nucleus — controls the cell.  Cytoplasm — where all the chemical reactions take place.  Cell membrane — controls what passes into and out of the cell. [One correct for one mark, all correct for two marks.] | |
| b i | 1 | Respiration. | |
| ii | 3 | Oxygen — used [One mark].  Glucose — used [One mark].  Carbon dioxide — made [One mark]. | |
| iii | 1 | Diffusion | |

**4.** a | 3 | E.g.

[Two marks if all points are plotted correctly, one mark if four or more points are plotted correctly. One mark for straight line of best fit]

b | 1 | D
c | 1 | Accept any answer between 6 and 8.

| Q | Marks | Correct answer |
|---|---|---|
| **5.** a | 2 | It is repelled by magnet A [One mark], so moves downwards away from it [One mark]. |
| b | 2 | If it's the wrong way up it will attract the small magnet [One mark], which will move in the wrong direction and give a result that's off the scale [One mark]. |
| c | 1 | So that the arm is balanced before any magnets are tested **OR** to increase the sensitivity / accuracy / precision of the pointer / so that the pointer moves more. |
| d | 1 | The stronger magnet will give a bigger reading / make the pointer move further up the scale. |

| Q | Marks | Correct answer |
|---|---|---|
| **6.** a | 2 | The water has become more acidic [One mark], because the universal indicator has turned from green (neutral) to orange (weak acid) [One mark]. |
| b | 2 | Ordinary air didn't affect the pH of the water after 2 minutes [One mark], because the universal indicator stayed green (neutral) [One mark]. |
| c | 2 | Becky's experiment showed that breathing into water made it more acidic [One mark], and Huang's showed that this was due to a substance in her breath and not just due to air bubbling through it [One mark]. |

| Q | Marks | Correct answer |
|---|---|---|
| **7.** a | 1 | diaphragm |
| b | 1 | Because the volume of the jar has increased/the pressure in the jar has decreased. |

*Answers*

| | | | |
|---|---|---|---|
| | c | 2 | The balloons would deflate [One mark], because the volume of the jar has decreased/the pressure in the jar has increased [One mark]. |
| | d | 1 | E.g. tar |

| | | | |
|---|---|---|---|
| 8. | a | 2 | Rock B [One mark], because its crystals are bigger due to it cooling more slowly/underground [One mark]. |
| | b | 2 | Marble — metamorphic. Limestone — sedimentary. Granite — igneous. [One mark one correct, two marks for all]. |

| | | | |
|---|---|---|---|
| 9. | a | 1 | friction **OR** air resistance |
| | b | 2 | *Tip:* They've done the first one for you here, so use that to your advantage and make sure your bars are the same width and in the same position within the space.<br><br>[One mark for two bars plotted correctly, two marks for all bars plotted correctly (including labels on x-axis).] |
| | c | 3 | E.g. different mass, different amounts of friction between floor and wheels, different amount of air resistance due to different shapes, rolled down slope from different heights [One mark for each]. |

| | | | |
|---|---|---|---|
| 10. | a | 1 | It is wasted as heat. |
| | b | 1 | The price of each bulb. |
| | c | 2 | She won't have to bother changing it so often [One mark] and less $CO_2$ is produced by the low power bulbs [One mark]. |
| | d | 1 | 20% of 60 = (60 ÷ 100) × 20 = 12 watt |

| | | | |
|---|---|---|---|
| 11. | a | 1 | 120 N |
| | b | 1 | The force from the string is not balanced **OR** It is pushed by the string **OR** Potential energy is converted to kinetic energy **OR** Energy is transferred to the arrow from the bow. |
| | c | 1 | They are at right angles to each other **OR** They are in perpendicular directions |
| | d | 1 | It would have a larger surface area **OR** Because pressure is force divided by area |

| | | | |
|---|---|---|---|
| 12. | a | 1 | Because the same atoms are present. |
| | b  i | 1 | Oxygen |
| | ii | 1 | 2 g |
| | c | 1 | Zinc oxide |

| | | | |
|---|---|---|---|
| 13. | a | 1 | Liquid to gas (accept 'evaporation') |
| | b | 3 | Chemical [One mark] to heat/light [One mark] to kinetic. [One mark] |
| | c | 2 | Any two from: natural gas, coal, oil, nuclear [One mark each]. |

| | | | |
|---|---|---|---|
| 14. | a | 3 | P — breastbone **OR** sternum [One mark]. Q — ribs [One mark]. R — backbone **OR** spine **OR** vertebral column [One mark]. |
| | b  i | 1 | Protection. |
| | ii | 1 | Support **OR** movement. |

| | | | |
|---|---|---|---|
| 15. | | 4 | [One mark for every four squares filled in correctly]<br><br>*Tip:* It's amazing how many people get these questions wrong, because all you really need to know is that a more reactive metal takes the place of a less reactive one in a solution. And the reactivity series is right there, showing you who's more reactive than who. |

# KS3 Science Paper 3A

| Q | Marks | Correct answer | Useful tips |
|---|---|---|---|
| 1. a | 1 | Lamp **OR** bulb. | |
| b | 1 | Ammeter. | |
| c | 1 | Battery/Cell. | |
| d | 1 | Voltmeter. | |

| | | |
|---|---|---|
| 2. | 4 | Stomach acid — red — 1 [One mark].  Soap powder — blue — 10 [One mark].<br>Lemon juice — orange — 3 [One mark].  Salt water — green — 7 [One mark]. |

| | | |
|---|---|---|
| 3. a | 4 | **A** - sperm tube, **B** - penis, **C** - urethra, **D** - testis, **E** - bladder<br>[All correct for four marks, two correct for one mark, three correct for two marks, four correct for three marks] |
| b | 1 | Sperm |

| Q | Marks | Correct answer | Useful tips |
|---|---|---|---|
| 4. a | 2 | 96 Nm   [One mark for 96, one mark for Nm  (OR can be 9600 Ncm)] | *TIPS: Moments and energy transfer in all their glory in one question. So make sure you've got the answers right. If not practise and practise again and again.* |
| b | 2 | 12 m/s   [One mark for 12, one mark for m/s  (OR can be 1200 cm/s)] | |
| c | 1 | 300 Hz   [No mark if more than one frequency circled] | |
| d | 1 | chemical/potential energy in the bell-ringer  **OR** chemical energy  (No mark for 'energy in the bell-ringer') | |
| | 1 | transferred via the rope/mechanically  **OR**  transferred to the bell  **OR**  transferred from the rope<br>**OR**  to the rope  **OR**  potential/kinetic energy in the bell  (No mark for 'to kinetic energy,' or 'to potential energy') | |
| | 1 | as bell swings, kinetic energy changes to potential energy<br>**OR**  as bell swings, potential energy changes to kinetic energy  (No mark for if the bell swinging is not mentioned) | |
| | 1 | transferred by sound  **OR**  becomes sound energy  **OR**  transferred to surroundings/sound/the air/people's ears | |
| | | [One mark for each of the four potential points with a maximum of 3 marks.  The points must be made in a logical order.] | |

| | | |
|---|---|---|
| 5. a | 2 | From top to bottom, the column should read: 20, 24, 29, 21, 28 (Lose one mark for each mistake) |
| b | 2 | Any two of: always use the same mass of cornflakes, always use the same volume of water, keep the boiling tube the same distance from the burning cornflakes, keep the thermometer at the same height in the boiling tube [One mark each]. |
| c | 1 | They could repeat the experiment several times and take an average. |
| d | 1 | They could insulate the apparatus **OR** use a wider-bottomed container for the water (to absorb more of the heat from the cornflakes). |

| | | |
|---|---|---|
| 6. a | 1 | Distillation. |
| b | 1 | They have different boiling points **OR** alcohol boils at a lower temperature than water does. |
| c | 1 | The alcohol is cooling and turning back into a liquid / condensing. |
| d | 2 | Brandy [One mark], because the alcohol in the wine evaporates off first and runs into the container of brandy [One mark]. |

| Q | Marks | Correct answer | Useful tips |
|---|---|---|---|
| 7. a | 1 | Attrition **OR** Erosion.  [One mark for each] | *TIPS: All this stuff about rocks might seem like geography, but it's a very popular science question.* |
| b | 2 | They are smoothed and rounded.  They get smaller.  [One mark for each] | |
| c | 1 | Stage 4:  Deposition / Sedimentation. | |
| | 1 | Stage 5:  Compression/Compaction. | |

| 8. | a i | 2 | Plastic **OR** wood [One mark], because it is not a good conductor of heat so will stop his hand being burnt [One mark]. |
| | ii | 2 | Copper **OR** steel [One mark], because it has a high melting point **OR** because it is not flammable [One mark]. |
| | b | 1 | The smoke is hotter than the air in the room, meaning it is less dense, so it rises — straight up the chimney. |
| | c | 1 | The heat energy is given out in the form of a wave by radiation. |

Tip: That's right, there was more than one correct answer. That might happen now and again, so don't let it confuse you — don't sit there for hours trying to come up with a reason why wood wouldn't be any good as a handle.

| 9. | a | 1 | Any one of: wear goggles, use a heat-proof mat, handle the hot crucible with tongs [One mark]. |
| | b | 2 | Element: 1 **OR** 2 [One mark]. Compound: 4 [One mark]. |
| | c i | 1 | Iron sulfide. |
| | ii | 1 | FeS. |
| | d | 1 | 8.8 g. |

| 10. | a i | 2 | $CO_2$ **OR** $H_2O$ **OR** CO **OR** C. One mark for any of these up to 2 marks. |
| | ii | 2 | Water droplets on the jar **OR** Soot **OR** Light / heat given off. One mark for any of these up to 2 marks. |
| | b i | 2 | The carbon dioxide level decreases. The oxygen level rises. |
| | ii | 2 | Photosynthesis stops. Respiration continues **OR** The changes would reverse. [One mark for each.] |
| | c i | 1 | Chloroplasts. |
| | ii | 1 | Nucleus. |

TIPS: If you find you're running out of time in these practice papers think about how long you spend on each question. Don't spend ages on one question, especially if it's only worth a mark or two. Get on with the rest and come back to it later.

| 11. | a | 2 | The turbine converts wind energy to kinetic energy. The generator converts kinetic energy to electrical energy. [One mark for each] |
| | b | 1 | The wind can not be used up. |
| | c | 1 | Tidal energy **OR** Solar power **OR** Biomass **OR** Hydroelectric **OR** Geothermal. [One mark for any one of these.] |

| 12. | a | 2 | Any two from: rabbit, mouse, sparrow [One mark each]. |
| | b | 2 | Any two from: fox, weasel, buzzard [One mark each]. |
| | c | 1 | The Sun. |
| | d i | 1 | Weasel numbers would drop because they would have less food [One mark]. (No mark if the answer suggests the weasels die.) |
| | ii | 1 | The number of mice would go up because there would be more food for them **OR** because there are now fewer weasels **OR** mouse numbers would drop because the weasels would eat more of them now that there are no rabbits [One mark] (Mark only awarded if the reason explains the effect on numbers. The mark can also be awarded if the same answer concludes that mouse numbers would stay the same overall.) |

| 13. | | 2 | The elephant's weight is spread out over a much bigger area [One mark], so it exerts less pressure on the floor than Mrs Lightfoot's heels which cover a much smaller area [One mark]. |

| 14. | a | 1 | 800 × 10 = 8000 N. |
| | b | 2 | Pressure = force ÷ area. Pressure = 8000 ÷ 0.25 = 32 000 N/m² [One mark for correct answer, one mark for correct units] |

# KS3 Science Paper 3B

| Q | Marks | Correct answer | Useful tips |
|---|---|---|---|
| 1. | 3 | Team A pulls with a total force of 27 N + 24 N + 21 N = 72 N [One mark]. Team B pulls with a total force of 19 N + 32 N + 23 N = 74 N [One mark]. So team B will win (because they pull with a greater total force) [One mark]. | *Tip: Dead simple this — to find the total force in any direction, just add all the forces going that way together.* |

| Q | | | Marks | Correct answer |
|---|---|---|---|---|
| 2. | a | | 1 | 'It affects the nervous system.' **should be circled.** |
| | b | i | 2 | The chance of having an accident increases, the rate of increase gets faster the more alcohol is in the blood. **One mark for just saying 'it increases'.** |
| | | ii | 1 | 'Alcohol increases the time it takes for a person to react'. **should be circled.** |

| Q | | Marks | Correct answer |
|---|---|---|---|
| 3. | a | 3 | Nucleus — Cell Membrane — Cytoplasm **[One mark for each]** |
| | b | 2 | Cell wall **OR** Vacuole **OR** Chloroplasts. **[One mark for any of these up to 2 marks]** |
| | c | 1 | Tissue **OR** organ |

| Q | | Marks | Correct answer |
|---|---|---|---|
| 4. | a | 1 | Oxygen. |
| | b | 1 | Oxygen. |
| | c | 1 | 6 + 12 + 6 = 24. |

| Q | | Marks | Correct answer |
|---|---|---|---|
| 5. | a | 3 | [One mark for sensible scale on axes, one mark for correctly plotting points, one mark for good line of best fit] |
| | | | *Tip: Don't worry if you didn't give the actual speed of the marble. There's only one mark for the question and they didn't ask you to calculate anything, so saying the speed is constant should be fine. Well done if you did work it out though. Smarty-pants.* |
| | b | 1 | They show that the marble falls at a constant speed (of 5 cm/s). |

| Q | | Marks | Correct answer |
|---|---|---|---|
| 6. | a | 3 | Hydrochloric acid — calcium chloride — calcium hydroxide [One mark]. Sulfuric acid — copper sulfate — copper hydroxide [One mark]. Nitric acid — iron nitrate — iron hydroxide [One mark]. |
| | b | 1 | Hydrochloric acid. |
| | c | 1 | Nitric acid. |

| Q | | Marks | Correct answer |
|---|---|---|---|
| 7. | a | 2 | as chemical energy [One mark] in Matt's muscles [One mark] |
| | b | 1 | the molecules hit the walls of the balloon **OR** they bounce off the walls/balloon |
| | c | 1 | they speed up/get faster |
| | d | 1 | they'll hit the wall of the balloon more often/harder/faster **OR** more collisions with balloon **No mark for 'more collisions' or 'molecules move faster'** |

*Answers*

| 8. | a | 2 | Methane + oxygen $\rightarrow$ carbon dioxide + water [Take away one mark for each mistake or omission]. |
|---|---|---|---|
| | b | 2 | More carbon dioxide [One mark] and less oxygen [One mark]. |
| | c | 1 | C. |

*Tip: Any compound of just hydrogen and carbon produces water and carbon dioxide when it burns.*

| 9. | a | 3 | 20 Nm. *100 × 0.2 = 20 Nm.* [One mark for working, one for units, one for answer.] |
|---|---|---|---|
| | b i | 1 | 20 Nm. *(It balances the moment of the 100 N force.)* |
| | ii | 1 | 25 N. *20 ÷ 0.8 = 25 N.* |
| | iii | 2 | 20 N/cm$^2$. *100 ÷ 5 = 20 N/cm$^2$.* [One mark for units, one for answer.] |

*TIPS: When you do these mathsy questions you've got to remember the units.*

| 10. | a | 1 | Carbon dioxide + water $\rightarrow$ glucose + oxygen. |
|---|---|---|---|
| | b | 1 | By counting the number of bubbles produced in a given time. |
| | c | 1 | Repeat the experiment and take an average of his readings. |
| | d | 1 | Chlorophyll. |
| | e | 1 | Light energy **OR** sunlight |

| 11. | a | 4 | P — ovary [One mark]. Q — oviduct **OR** Fallopian tube [One mark]. R — uterus **OR** womb [One mark]. S — cervix [One mark]. |
|---|---|---|---|
| | b | 1 | An ovary. |
| | c | 1 | Day 14. |
| | d | 1 | Its lining thickens. |

| 12. | a | 3 | Similar to: |
|---|---|---|---|

ray of sunlight

spectrum

red
orange
yellow
green
blue
indigo
violet

glass prism

[One mark for showing the direction of the ray changing correctly, one mark for showing that the ray spreads out, one mark for giving a spectrum of colours]

| | b | 2 | Dispersion [One mark] and refraction [One mark]. |
|---|---|---|---|

| 13. | a | 2 | Heating the coin gives the particles more energy, so they vibrate more strongly [One mark]. This means that each particle takes up a slightly bigger volume, so the coin expands [One mark]. |
|---|---|---|---|
| | b | 2 | The particles of rose-water had more energy after heating [One mark], so they turned into gas particles (which could spread around the room) more readily [One mark]. |
| | c | 2 | They both involve the particles of the substances [One mark] changing their behaviour after being given more energy [One mark]. |

| 14. | a | 2 | Lit: A, B [One mark]. Not lit: C, D [One mark]. |
|---|---|---|---|
| | b | 3 | Close switch S1 [One mark]. Open switch S2 [One mark]. Remove the voltmeter **OR** connect the voltmeter in parallel not in series [One mark]. |

| 15. | a | 2 | By evaporating all the water [One mark] to see if a solid is left behind (because KCl will only be left if it was dissolved in the water) [One mark]. |
|---|---|---|---|
| | b | 1 | There was no reaction because potassium is more reactive than magnesium. |
| | c | 2 | A secondary source [One mark] because their conclusions are based on an error [One mark]. |

SHB33